The Incredible Hides In Every House

Imprint

A Collection of
Short Stories
& Poetry

In aid of
Habitat for
Humanity

Edited by
Nuala Ní Dhomhnaill

THE INCREDIBLE HIDES IN EVERY HOUSE
A Collection of Short Stories and Poetry
in aid of Habitat for Humanity

First published September 2005 by
The Irish Writers' Centre
Parnell Square, Dublin 1

The Incredible Hides in Every House the collection
© copyright The Irish Writers' Centre 2005
Named Short Story / Poem © copyright named writer 2005
(for full copyright details see Copyright Notices page 182)

ISBN 0-9550588-0-5

A CIP catalogue record for this title is available from the British Library

Typeset by *Aad*
Cover design by *Scott Burnett, Aad*
Printed in Belgium by *Snoeck Ducaju & Zoon*

The
Incredible
Hides
In
Every
House

"A symphony of voices with one thing in common - all striving for the truth. Their endeavour leaves a song in the heart."
Justine McCarthy *Irish Independent.*

"Quirky, inventive, funny and often moving; a beguiling collection of poems and stories from the new Ireland by writers with a fresh outlook and something to say."
Frank McNally *Irish Times*

"A fascinating compilation of new voices and ways of seeing. It reveals much about the strange and sometimes lovely place that is Ireland now, its morals and manners, its preoccupations and mysteries. More even than that, the book is great fun. Reading it is like finding yourelf at a party full of interesting people, each of whom has things to say that are new and striking or funny. And some of the writing is very beautiful, too. I found it hard to put down."
Joseph O'Connor *Novelist*

Contents

Acknowledgements

The efforts, encouragement and support of many people and organisations have helped to bring this project to fruition and we wish to express our gratitude to them. Our goal of raising funds for and awareness of the work of Habitat for Humanity in Ireland could not have been achieved without your collective generosity. Thank you.

Nuala Ní Dhomhnaill kindly edited the collection and donated an original poem and short story. We thank her for supporting this project from the beginning and for her honesty, hard work and endorsement. It's been great.

Cathal McCabe, Director, Irish Writers' Centre, was most helpful in backing the project from the start and agreeing to publish this book. The staff at the Centre were obliging one and all. The Irish Writers' Centre allowed us to use its rooms free of charge; an invaluable asset for conducting workshops and meetings.

We are grateful to Habitat for Humanity for their enthusiasm towards this project throughout the process.

Scott Burnett at Angry Associates designed the cover and his colleague Johnny Kelly managed production and distribution. Their sound advice and professional expertise was invaluable.

The Writers, The Incredible Hides in Every House, 2005.

Sponsors

Thanks to our corporate sponsors
Gerard McCaughey, Chief Executive,
Canada Life, Century Homes,
Eagle Star, EBS, Ecocem, Fyffes,
Hawthorn Properties Belfast, Keith
Simpson and Associates, New Ireland
Assurance and Patann Ltd. Their
kind donations funded capital costs
associated with this project.

Introduction

Picture to yourself how it all began. It is a gloomy evening in September. It may or may not be raining. But whatever way you look at it, the weather has turned. The light is yellow and slant, the shadows are very long. We are settling in for the long haul up until Christmas, the shortening of the days, the lengthening of the nights.

A group of twenty-one complete strangers meets for the first time in a tall room in the Georgian building in Parnell Square that houses the Irish Writers' Centre. I am facilitating the group and full of the dull fear that prevents me from being a really social person, the free-floating anxiety that I always feel before meeting a new group of people. Already I think we are too many, and that it will be hard to manage such a diverse group, but I am counting on past memories of such groupings and the inevitable wastage that will occur. By the end of the course there should be about ten people left, the tough and final hard core.

This is one of the many writing courses that have been advertised by the Irish Writers' Centre to take place in Autumn 2004. Apart from a short course with the Bealtaine group, in the month of that name last summer, it is absolutely yonks since I have been asked to give a workshop at the Irish Writers' Centre. Now I have been asked what I would like to do and I have suggested a creative writing course for complete beginners, in both prose and poetry, Irish and English. I don't know what to expect. I dare say nobody else does, either. The first obstacle is the furniture. The tables and chairs are divided up into three different groups. As far as I am concerned this won't work; it will mitigate against a proper group dynamic. A circle would be best, but we still need the tables to write on. At the expense of not being able to see the individual faces at the far end so clearly, I decide a long mass of table would be the best configuration. As we all get together to move the furniture around the ice is broken. I think it will work.

We introduce ourselves and I set down the basic rules that I think are the absolute minimum that will ensure we will get some work done: an assignment each week; it must be typed up and photocopied so that there will be a copy to put in front of each participant every week. The Centre will help us with this so if you don't have copies you can come in a little bit early and get them done before the class. All I can see is a sea of faces. I am short-sighted and not particularly good with names and it will take some time and an acquaintance with their work before I am able to place people. Already I notice that most look expectant, some are guarded, others seem downright sardonic. Then to get things started I bring out a heap of postcards, some of the thousands that I have collected from every museum I have ever visited throughout the world. Many of them are of rotund goddess figures from the Neolithic in Anatolia. Others are pictures of Japanese pottery, or well-known icons of the Western visual canon, though none of them is the Mona Lisa. Too easy. Too clichéd. 'Right,' I say, 'let's get to work. Choose a picture and you have a half an hour to write something about it.' 'Write how much?' 'Oh, about a page.' I know this is unexpected, that I have caught most people on the hop. Nobody thought they would be writing on the spot, there and then. I know it is something very difficult to do, but don't let anything on. A half an hour later time is up, and now everyone has to read out what they have written. I also know that for many this is even more difficult, but we had better jump in at the deep end. To give people their due, everyone has obviously tried their best. Some are good. Some are better. Some are already surprisingly interesting. I think I may have uncovered a nest of secret scribblers, people who have been writing for years, but have hidden what they write in the lowest drawer of their cupboards or even in a box under the bed. Good. This is step one. The next step of what I am here to do is to get people to the stage where they can share their writing with others, and learn to take public responsibility for what they write. But we definitely have somewhere to start from. Already I think I am onto a good thing.

The assignment for this week is to type up what has been written and to make photocopies of it for next week. Also to take another postcard and to write something about that as well. Already people are hearing what is my constant admonition. Type it up. It is the nearest I hope I will ever come to a negative comment, because I believe my job is to create a nurturing and safe environment where people can gradually learn to criticise each other, but not in a destructive or personal way. This is based on a deep personal belief that where groups of people are involved, the whole can often be greater than the parts, and that a good group dynamic can get people to a stage where they are not afraid of criticism, self-criticism, and the energy and self-confidence it takes to make a quantum leap onto a new plateau of learning. This is not something you can will into being. There are so many imponderables. It is often just luck that a particular group of people gels. Still there is much that I can do. When I myself was starting off I had some disastrous personal experiences of workshops which spiralled down into negative vortexes of tit-for-tat spatting and mutual recrimination. This has to be avoided at all costs.

Before leaving I mention that it is a good idea to keep a class journal. That I myself, being very old fashioned and low-tech, actually keep a big hardbacked notebook, but that anyone can use whatever recording method they like. I can see already that some people are much more media-canny than I. For God's sake, there is even one woman typing everything into a laptop as I speak.

And that was that. The first meeting. In those first weeks I brought in more pictures and various objects that might help to start up the writing process. One week it was even a bag of supermarket apples. To be looked at, smelled, eaten – anything that might stir the imagination, the apple being in our culture something as deep and imponderable as Eve. I found to my amazement that not everybody likes apples. Some downright hate them. It didn't matter what the feeling or opinion was. What was important was that it got written down. Later on we trawled through a great variety of literary forms together. Experimental novels that most people hated were read and passed around. Then there was a buzz of haikus, two weeks at least on the sonnet. Gradually people settled down to the form they liked best. They even taught me more than a thing or two – like the new form that is taking hold, and best epitomised by the Fish competition – the short-short story of up to 250 words. By the time we came to the end of the course, before Christmas, a self-defining and self-sustaining sub-culture had grown up around the class, and yes, we were down to between twelve and ten, the inevitable and serious hard core.

What I had not anticipated in my wildest dreams was the way this group of writers would continue in my absence. They just took off like a rocket. There was no stopping them. They met together and exchanged criticism and confidences. Roughly once a month I received a large package of new writing in the house down in Ventry where I was now staying. About once a month I came up to Dublin and went through the work with them one by one. The Writers' Centre very kindly provided the premises, usually our old familiar room. Gradually stylistic preferences and literary personas emerged. Caroline Lynch specialised in poetry and the title of this book comes from an excellent poem of hers. Kathleen Murray broke out with a wild and wonderful imagination. Iain Wilkinson developed his character 'Joe', sardonic and slightly bewildered by suburban living. Emily Maher wrote stories and poems of the new hardnosed Ireland. Lisa Allen had a great line in Dorothy Parker-style urban lyrics. Ian Mitchell went at it great guns and brought a needful Northern perspective. Yvonne Garrigan brought a disenchanted and unblinkered sense of reality. Jack Murray wrote of small-time and rural Ireland and its necessary shift into the city, with all the different kinds of nostalgias that this entails. It seems specious and trite of me to attempt to characterise in a short sentence the multifaceted themes and styles which different people took up. This book is the result of their talent and endeavour, which I soon discovered was not confined to literary matters, but to organisational powers and altruistic concerns as well.

Shortly before we broke up for Christmas and the course was formally over the idea of bringing out a book and of doing it for charity came up in conversation. But it didn't just linger and languor there, in talk alone. A very positive energy took over. The choice of Habitat for Humanity as the particular charity was the result of a long and agonising process, but seemed finally to best fit all the different opinions of the options that presented themselves. The overall theme of 'Home' was also general enough to satisfy everyone. It has both an international and an Irish dimension, and is of perennial interest and importance. The pieces chosen for inclusion clustered around this theme and were organised as much as possible to highlight it. After all, not everyone has a home to go to. Therefore the Afterword, from Deirdre Barry of Habitat for Humanity, is especially fitting, as it clearly describes the aims and methods of her particular charity.

This group of writers has now outgrown my services. Many will go on, I feel assured, to make a name in the literary revival that started in Ireland at the end of the last century and seems in no way like abating. I will always feel delighted and proud that I had a small part in setting them off on their literary adventures.

Nuala Ní Dhomhnaill
Lake Bafa, Turkey
June 2005

In Every House
Caroline Lynch

The incredible hides in every house,
sometimes behind soft furs in a wardrobe
or in the twist of magic bedknob.

But we have found it here in the hallway
and we are ready to jump the stream running
under the closed door of the dining room;

to enter the strange garden on the other side
made from paper grass and cut-out trees –
home to a little red fox we all watch trot across

the dim colours of a world pressed for too long
inside a child's forgotten storybook.
A confusion of hands grasp for each other

to form a chain of children jumping clear
and when it is done, and the garden is gained
I am left behind, I am still on this side.

Too late now to leap – there is something
behind the dining room door, it is opening and
she hovers out, huge, framed, horrible and green;

the Mona Lisa. I run into the sitting room
to my mother in an armchair, she is talking to
my great-aunt, who is dead. My mother looks

at me, she has such a strange smile. I go no closer.
She vanishes and reappears, again and then again.
The incredible is gone. This is the terrible

that hides in every house.

The Living Room
Caroline Lynch

Evening comes down the chimney like ash and settles mother-soft
and grey on the corner of the living room that all day has quivered
under the drooped eye of the armchair that I pulled out especially
for this. This is the inventory of my mind accounting itself: a blister
pack to burst, a ring to pull off with a crack, a nest built in the back
of my neck where I fall asleep. There is a new measurement for this
sort of time – half hours of being forgotten when no one, not even
anyone-at-all, calls. The chair has a hold of my head, legs curl over
arms and air slips out of its skin, almost – if I could just unbreathe
for long enough. Later, when the sickness has passed, I see myself
very clearly as lost, off the grid completely, off the ambulance's
lit-up map of night emergencies, somewhere else for now, waiting
to wail and crackle into being.

Rule of Thumb
Caroline Lynch

I'm sliding down now, down the scale of opposites.
The last opposition is your thumb, resting there
by that measurement, testing the momentum of my
plunge. Some days ago you bit off a piece of skin
hung from your nail, and now there is a hot bulge
of infection. You wince when I press the marker down.
We are a strange team, bent over this old yardstick,
neither of us knowing what the other one means
when we speak to each other in abandoned degrees.

Flashback
Caroline Lynch

When this photo was taken I was already drunk.
I hadn't yet told the person who took it
to fuck off. But I would before the night was out.

Not that I was faking the smile, the big chunks
of good-time, bold-as-brass, knock-it-back looks
with my sister, who could down four drinks about

the time I'd be starting my third – the sunken
ice tinkling in the cold glass, the lemon hooked
by my finger, a good bitter suck in my mouth

and my purse shaken loose of its change, dunked
on the counter, rolled to the till. I don't ever puke,
I just gag on my mood. The toilet floor's grout

between tiles was caked dirty-white. I hunkered
there making a show of myself, writing the truth
that I couldn't do this – the hang-ups, the doubts

all making their marks. Afterwards I slunk
into the old dark and stayed for months, rocked
to sleep in a hood, a fist shoved into a shout.

No photos taken then. Just this, smiling and drunk
tilting in – being told by the flash that he took it,
that it would be framed. And that what came next

could be cut out.

Eating Each Other
Caroline Lynch

The hear-no-evil, speak-no-evil brigade go about the daily business
of shredding papers assiduously with teeth, eating volumes of print
for breakfast, and preparing for the evening editions at six by slowly
rubbing their ruined stomachs gently, anti-clockwise, with bleach.

I crack the top of my egg, and instead of a yellow yolk inside there is
a little man, liquefied with grief. What will I do with this? I ask them
while they sit chewing columns of disaster. Their arms stretch across
and they dip the rippings of some scandal into him even as his mouth

drips open on the table.

Turning Home
Caroline Lynch

My grandfather is lying like a newborn
and will be going into the earth soon.
His hands have lost their lifelines,
smoother than baby's and papery
with no print on them, no soil on them.
Wrist deep in fields
he took home his land beneath his fingernails
and each season turned in his palm.
Winter turned in his palm.
Outside the ground is warming and rising
but the world in his hands has sunk away.
The sun is going down and he is turning home
away from the house and down to the fields.

The Dream at the End of the World
Caroline Lynch

From motes floating in her eye she dreamed us.
She dreamed the mountains from misty atoms
and wove fog with sleep and so there were sheep.
The lamb ran from her lashes and it leaped
across her stare into the thin whiteness of air.
A choir of raindrops hung quivering like truth
on quiet grass, never opening its soft mouth
while the loose, long tongue of the lying stream
towards morning woke her from her dream
with a quick lick, slicking stones wickedly.

She lay in her dark bed alone, the image
of us leaving her still with her – the midges
round our heads like haloes, our distant home,
our long journey and the trouble to come –
until the newly drawn horizon hid us at dawn.
She opened the curtains, created the world
and made a pink throat for the song of a bird,
but no one was there to hear her confess
that the flaring star she chose as our compass
was dying, was dimming, and soon it would be darker

than it was in the beginning.

The Match
Caroline Lynch

I told the woodsman that hurleys are made of ash
and about the clash that is the cliché of all that.

By Salisbury Cathedral he explained the rules
of cricket – enthusiastic inflection, lovely round

vowels bowled across grass. Then I picked up
a sliotar on a flick of air that I held like a hurley

and pucked the tight wad of nothing, high, long
over the cathedral spire's great struts of Irish oak.

The Abandoned House Mouse
Caroline Lynch

*(After the evacuation of St Kilda
the house mouse became extinct on the island.)*

When they left, the rump of a great cat
settled on the roof like it was a cushion
and the silence in the house was huge.
We were alone
and we dragged ourselves, thinner and
thinner, through the cupboards emptied
of all flour, our eyes drier than crumbs.
They were gone
and we could die wherever we wanted,
mostly floating the trance of the kitchen's
linoleum floor, its blue patterns gulping –
We were gone
and the house, squatting in its sorrow,
squinted out and saw the sea's green jaw
flexing its appetite like a winter storm.

Moving
Caroline Lynch

1. My dog to be dug up
   from the back garden
   and his bones brought with me
2. The rainbow outside
   to be taken down
   and re-framed in the new sky
3. All ornamental dust
   to be packed up
   and stacked particle by article
4. Next-door's apple trees
   and piano-playing
   to be sent on before me
5. The ants under the patio
   to be ordered
   march on and follow me
6. The attic to be flat-packed
7. My bedroom to be bubble-wrapped
8. Things that must be left labelled;
   Wait For My Return

My Fingertip, Malcolm's Eye, Ettie and the Chinaman
Kathleen Murray

A thirty-minute car ride got me from my home in Tantallon to Halifax. That first thirty minutes felt like leaving. Once I was alone on the bus from Halifax, it felt like I was going somewhere. Working my way across the country, mostly in hotels and tip jobs, I reached Vancouver by fall. Although I had no particular training, I landed a job in an old hotel, now a hostel for people with mental health problems. Mostly the residents were schizophrenic but two had drug-related brain damage. One woman had a disease slowly destroying her memory, soaking it out like blotting paper and ink. They all got an appointment every second month with the doctor, based in a clinic up the road. He looked them over, gave them an injection if required and signed off the prescriptions. On payday, we cashed our cheques, ate Chinese food and drank whiskey in a late-night bar on Guerrero and Oak. It was a members-only bar for taxi drivers, backing onto the railway line down by the waterfront. You paid $10 membership fee at the door; anyone could drink there. Gerda, the owner, was an alcoholic. Once a week she got drunk while her daughter served. End of night, Gerda would be carried upstairs by the girl. Sometimes a customer would help if they were sober enough to care. I helped one night but she tried to bite me on the stairs. Her daughter showed me bite scars all over her forearms.

I was working over Christmas and didn't make it home. I phoned the family occasionally but gradually fell out of contact. Fourteen months after I left home my younger brother came to visit me. As I was the only girl in the family and he was the eldest of the boys, we were close. He was just going on eighteen but I got him into the bar because of my regular custom. He told me about the family, the farm, the local hockey team, his girlfriends. I told him about places in the city to get coffee after midnight, what types of pills to avoid, how to use ice coins in the electricity meter, some of the dislocating, disconnected things people said to me during the day. At one point, I became animated and pinched his arm too tightly. My eyes were bright; my heart was pumping blood, thumping. I was taken by how big our little world had become. We were both drunk. He told me I was hurting his arm and we laughed at that and at the people shuffle-dancing to Patsy on the jukebox.

Richard joined us. Richard the on–off glue fiend. On, he wore huge headphones and carried an old reel-to-reel on the street. Although he didn't live in the hostel, he hung out with our guys. Tonight he was headphones- and glue-free. Renee, his girlfriend, was with him. She was new to me, maybe new to town, maybe just this part of town. She was quiet and could drink. They'd been there a couple of hours already. Richard went to the bar to get a round.

'Renee is pregnant,' she said, 'with Richie's baby.'

I knew she was talking about herself. My brother got lost with the third person thing. I congratulated her and my brother used the change on the table to pick out a song on the jukebox for the occasion. Conversation had moved on from the baby to something else before his songs came up. The first song was the Temptations' 'Ready for Love'. It wasn't country or rock but it sounded fine. Renee put her hand on his arm, 'Renee likes to dance.'

They were dancing when Richard came back with the drinks. I remembered the baby thing and congratulated him. He looked tired. Getting a drink at the end of the night was hard work. Increased demand, decreased service.

'That baby's dead. It's dead in her belly. The doctor says she has to carry to the end. Some medical reason they can't take it out now. I don't know why. She won't get any bigger. She'll stay the same till the end. Maybe the baby was developing tastes we couldn't afford.'

I couldn't think of much to say. 'Did she want the baby?'

'She already has a daughter. She doesn't get to see her much. In foster care back east.'

We chatted while we watched the dancing. Richard only ever talked about music. He had a huge collection of tapes. My brother was duck-walking the floor to the saxophone solo and Renee was doing fancy handclaps. They looked good.

I couldn't go to the bus station with my brother the next day because I was on an early shift so I said goodbye when I said goodnight. I was pretty used to working a shift with a hangover, sometimes even a double. When I buzzed to get in to work, James, the graveyard shift guy, used the intercom to give me a running commentary on the activities of a cockroach he was holding captive, swimming in the dregs in his coffee mug. He locked himself into the office every night around four to snort. Each morning in the margins of the logbook, alongside notes on residents' nocturnal activity, he would sketch a picture of the biggest, craziest cockroaches he had seen the night before.

* * * * *

Ettie believed she couldn't breathe. She self-medicated with cough mixture and raw garlic and the smell from her breath made me retch. Every surface in her room was sticky and marked from old cough bottles. In the morning, waking her up from deep snores, her first words were 'I can't breathe.' This continued all day with only slight variations. Sometimes we would reason with her, offer reassurances, but mostly there wasn't time. I would tell her 'If you can speak, then you can breathe. So can you breathe?'

'No.'

Logic removed me from her fear, my internal cooling system whilst Ettie overheated. She eventually worked it so we had to replace her standard single bed with a hospital bed. She cranked it up to sleep in a sitting position, because she was afraid to choke in her sleep. She had a cheap grey permed wig taken from another resident. It sat at an angle over her eye, propped up by her glasses. She never left the building much, in case she stopped breathing away from help. One day a man buzzed the intercom and said he had a date with Ettie. She left on his arm, wig straightened, cheeks rouged, saying coyly, 'He's a gentleman I used to know.' Maybe he was a gentleman. He drove his own car, dropped her back at nine and walked her to the door.

In the summer, one of the excursions was to fill the van with as many residents as could be moved and drive up to Yasgurs farm. We always referred to it as Yasgurs farm, so each time we started the trip we would sing the Joni Mitchell song. It was corny but it always got a cheer; repetition worked. The farm was a rehab place for drying out alcoholics. Our crew went up on day trips, shuffled around the yard, maybe helped with some fencing or animals, and paddled in the river. Some of the men liked the activities; mostly the women went for a change of scenery. It was a particularly hot summer. Every day we bought icelollies and used them as rewards and bribes; they became the second-most traded item after smokes. Ettie, for some reason, had begun to wear layers of clothes – vest, blouses, jackets, skirts, trousers, the whole nine yards. A few residents, mostly ex-panhandlers, layered their clothes for living on the street, so it wasn't unknown. Afterwards the doctor told us he had suspected Alzheimer's but he hadn't mentioned it to us. I don't think it would have made much difference. When the van came back that evening Ettie was missing. They searched the farm for weeks; we took turns going up with the van, even on our days off. It became the main event that summer. All the residents made an effort. Even some of the voices in their heads got involved with suggested locations and scenarios and messages from Ettie. A canoeist found her body down-river later. They identified her by her clothing and her head was bald.

*   *   *   *   *

Two things happened in one week; the kind of events that usually spread themselves over a couple of weeks to break the monotony. Malcolm was a regular visitor to the office, sometimes looking for a warm jacket or boots from the clothes pile, sometimes just to talk. He came in Monday afternoon, half-drunk but civil, and scored a pair of socks and smokes. Thursday, Malcolm was sitting in the outer office with a patch on his eye.

'What happened, Mal?'

'My eye is gone. A Indian took it out in a fight. All sewed up now, no problem. Still got one eye. Lucky wasn't nose – only have one nose. You got a smoke?'

My co-worker that day was a devout, clean-living French-Canadian Baptist. In theory he tried to foster a culture of restraint and moderation through prayer.

In practice, he got along by applying the letter of the law.

'Life is cheap, Mal, is it not, on the streets?' he said, 'but cigarettes cost and to buy cigarettes, you must pay for a packet and to pay you must earn. First help me sweep the canteen, then smokes.'

The next day, Friday, I lost the tip of the little finger on my right hand. To be honest I never felt connected to the joint or the loss of same. Bamboo, a local pimp, managed to get up into the office. He headed up the list of banned visitors, kept beside the CCTV monitor. A few women residents had worked for him on the street. Always ready to re-employ them if their condition stabilised, he liked to keep in touch. Once in the office he ranted about lost earnings, threatened to sue the Department of Welfare, declaimed the street cleaners who removed his stickers from the phone booths on the street, cursed the born-agains living across the way and finally zoned in on the staff of the hostel. He was staring at the list on the wall above my head. Did he recognise his own name? Could he read? When I told him to leave, his eyes cleared, focusing on me. I thought he was reaching in his pocket to take out his bamboo whistle. He took out a knife, pinned my hand to the table and cut off the first joint of the little finger on my right hand. I thought I was screaming but I had lost my voice. He was high and the sight of the blood freaked him; he cried the whole way down the stairs. Pete, my boss, drove me to the hospital. We had forgotten to bring my fingertip. At that stage I had taken some tablets from the medical supplies and a pink pill Pete had in his wallet for emergencies. My hand felt like liquid music. The doctor stitched it up to stop the tunes escaping through the hole. Someone else picked up my paycheque and we caught up with the others in the Chinese.

We had a lottery at the end of each month for meds residents had refused or forgotten to take. My number had come up. I was lying on a bed in a spare single room, on my lunch break, spaced on a combination of pills. Watching the sunlight throw a texture onto the stains on the ceiling, the sound of a radio in another room drifted in. Someone knocked on the door to call me to the office for a phone call. My brother was on the phone. At first his voice was clear as a bell. Gradually it changed as if the gong was wrapped in the corner of a baby's blanket; it had a warm quality. He asked about Renee and Richard but I hadn't seen them around, not since his visit. As the conversation progressed a line of ants was forming an orderly line on the desk. Their destination, my sandwich. My brother told me he had joined the US army. A neighbour told him it was a first-rate time to be a soldier as there was a good chance he would get to see some action. I hadn't given much thought to the war. As he said this, my head emptied like a school auditorium at the end of term. From a wall at one side, a line of ants emerged carrying a banner, with my brother's words on it – *Good Time To Sign Up Will Get Sent To War.* When they reached the other side, they turned and began creating a long black dissecting column heading home. The opposite side of the banner read – *Bad Time To Sign Up Will Get Sent To War.*

The last time we had met was at the bar on Guerrero and Oak. We had talked that night about taking a train together down the west coast, maybe see an armadillo. Every time I said the word armadillo, we laughed. I was fairly sure the trains went over the border, down the coast and we could make it all the way. That night came into my head and the words army and armadillo connected in my brain. Thinking of my brother safe in an armadillo shell in the middle of a war gave me comfort. Later, I wrapped the remainder of my sandwich up and brought it down to the canteen for disposal. We had to be strict about food in the bedrooms because of the ongoing cockroach infestation.

*   *   *   *   *

For a while after the Chinaman disappeared, we kept his room just the same way he left it. His bed was made, a towel folded on his sink. There was the English–Chinese dictionary on the desk, a pencil and pencil sharpener. Some residents required assistance with their personal hygiene; the Chinaman led a minimal, pristine existence. A few white shirts with yellowing collars and cuffs and a three-piece brown suit hung in his wardrobe. He owned a second, nearly identical suit; he must have put it on before he left. That day he had come down to the office to ask the staff to get his razor from the medicine cabinet. We kept anything valuable in there; prescription meds, smokes we were rationing, our own stash and his electric razor. He shaved every second day, bringing the razor up to his room and returning with it cleaned, a half hour later. It was the only electric razor in the building but he would not share. The major lice infestation, I went up to get his go-ahead to use the electric razor. He turned his dictionary over to the Chinese–English side. When he found the word he was searching for, he underlined it for me. Never.

Every day, the Chinaman methodically read his dictionary. We knew this because on hot days he would leave the door open for air and we could see him from the corridor, his table under the window facing the street, bent over, his finger slowly tracing the English word and then nodding at the Chinese definition. Sometimes, he would walk out as far as the park on the corner after lunch, sit on a bench, watch the basketball games, the dealing, the children and then walk back. He didn't converse so I don't know how much English he understood or was able to use. He had no prescribed medications and someone said he was a leftover from when the hostel was a paying hotel and the area a thriving Chinatown.

We didn't notice his absence initially and when we did, it did not seem possible he would leave without his razor. The dictionary and his razor seemed the more substantial part of his presence and personality. We presumed he would return for them. His dictionary was open at the page starting with *kimono* and ending with *knee*. What happened to the Chinaman when he reached the K's? For a time, I would take my lunch up to his room, bring up a radio and read the words on the page. I couldn't read the Chinese definitions. Looking at each word I tried to imagine what disturbance it could cause – kimono, kin, kinesis, king, kithara, kiss, knee. After a number of weeks, a new resident arrived and the room was cleared out. I kept the dictionary and marked the page, just in case. At home a couple of nights, I worked my way backwards and forwards from his page, but I gave up before I even got to the start of the K's and was barely into the J's. J's and K's can take on a life of their own. I sensed a wall of capital J's, J's with their flattops, rocking on their curves, an army all facing left. Little j's were like a web, a filigree mesh holding the J wall together. Maybe this happened to the Chinaman, letters escaping their moorings. Perhaps he looked out the window for a moment and when his eyes returned to the page the K's had joined the barricade, throwing themselves on their sides, the sawhorses adding their bulk. The Chinaman had to walk away, not turning to the next page or holding out for his electric razor. He never showed up again.

Afterwards I often thought of Ettie and the Chinaman and my fingertip and Malcolm's eye. Although they disappeared months apart, it is one photographic plate with multiple exposures. Ettie is floating on the surface of the river, bobbing along like a wooden doll, her wig straightened, her cheeks rouged, all odours washed away and the layers of clothes forming cushioning air pockets. Each time she says 'Can't breathe' it echoes and return to her fainter and fainter until the last echo sounds like 'breathe'. The Chinaman has joined her from a tributary further down; lying on his back stiff as a board, mute as a fish, his yellowing shirt buttoned up and his face clean-shaven. His eyes are steady and alert, looking up at the clouds and the mountains, deciphering shapes and symbols. My fingertip resembles a little perch, pointing forward, leading the way. Malcolm's eye is blue and vibrant rolling from side to side, taking in the scenery, occasionally winking at Ettie.

The World and Joe
Iain Wilkinson

Text Messages and Joe

Sitting in the inevitable traffic jam just to leave the bloody estate, Joe looks around him. Nothing to see, just the driveways of most of the houses already empty, cars all neatly lined up to get out. In front a car, behind a car, to the left a kerb with an unkempt grass verge, to the right a kerb with a neat grass verge. 'Who cuts the verges?' wonders Joe.

He flicks the radio from station to station. Drivel on the happy pop station, dreary politician lying for no reason on the news station, dreary presenter accusing politicians of lying on the news-as-pop station. He hits play on the CD player and enjoys his cocoon.

His mobile phone beeps and vibrates in its silly holder. A text message so early in the day could be from only one person.

[Wnt a vid dis evng] it says. From Cathy, his girlfriend. (Asking if he'd like to watch a video later in the day, just in case you don't speak the lingo).

He contemplates the appropriate response. Should he key in [Yes] and then have to have a series of messages about who'll get it and what kind of film. Or key in [Yes, and I'll get it] knowing he'll forget, or key in [Yes. You get it?] and hope she won't get annoyed that he wants her to do the fetching. Maybe just call her and discuss the options. Calling in response to a text message isn't cool though, not the done thing. Problem is he hates text, all that fiddling.

The queue moves forward three car lengths. Seems crazy to Joe to have to send a text. Cathy is sitting in her own car just four cars ahead after all. He could just lean out the window and give her the thumbs up. Or shout a message. She wouldn't be happy with that but it would be funny to walk up there and actually talk to her. Make a point about the laziness of the modern commuter.

He slips off the seat belt and opens his door. The passing cyclist takes a glancing blow from the door and hits the road with a crash. Joe freezes imagining the annoyances about to befall him. In front Cathy's car begins to pull away. Behind the first driver looks at him with accusing eyes. Several cars back someone honks a horn to register his displeasure at the delay. The cyclist stirs with an expensive moan.

The Nanny and Joe

'This must be your Room 101, Joe,' murmured Marion as she hovered behind him. 'Kids, parents, bullshit conversation, no singles and no prospect of going on to a pub. Not to mention drinking standing up – you must hate it.'

On the contrary, thought Joe, though he did give her a conspiratorial nod of the head. My birthday gift for the little tyke went down well and the whole stupid event is nearly over. Another half hour of this and I'm done for another year. Quick excuse, quick exit, see you all next year. This godparent stuff wasn't all that tough. All the pain was in the anticipation, the worry that your gift would be shown up as inappropriate or thoughtless. Maybe not expensive enough, or god forbid too expensive and showy. He'd fought back the temptation to buy the sprog a little motorbike or a whole playground as a mad gesture. He'd imagined the truck pulling up during the party and everyone gasping at his largesse.

'It's not so bad,' he replied, 'nice to see the little ones having some fun.'

Marion was clearly unimpressed. In the corner of the living room, barely visible through the French windows, Joe noticed a morose woman in her forties. She may even have been crying.

'Hopefully I look a bit happier than the poor devil in there. Whose mother is she?'

Marion gave a snort. 'She's nobody's mother, you plonker, she's the nanny for the O'Donnell kid.'

'And why is she so unhappy – tell me she doesn't hate kids? Maybe she just doesn't like parties?'

'On the contrary, my dear cynical Joe, she loves them. However the youngest of her charges has just cleared his fourth birthday and he'll be off to school shortly. No need for nanny after that so no more job and no more home for Mary Poppins there.'

'You accuse me of cynicism!' Joe exclaimed. 'Have you no sympathy for her at all? No job, no house, cut off from the kids – what will she do next?'

'Jump in a river clutching a brick as far as I'm concerned. I've never understood these women who work with kids and have no lives. Creepy if you ask me, makes my skin crawl.'

Joe examined the woman but quickly looked away as her lonely eye met his.

The Spirits of the House and Joe

Joe opened the door and half-stepped inside. A certain amount of crap in there: old papers, tools, paint tins stacked at the back, an old briefcase he'd not used for years, a few coats hanging, an umbrella that he never touched, a half-deflated football, a golf club, a hoover, a drying rack for clothes he couldn't tumble dry. Around the rubbish were empty patches of carpeted floor. The cosiness of the virgin carpet appealed to him. It was still the original colour, no chance for it to fade in the sunlight or have stuff dropped on it. No wine had been dripped onto it.

He reached in and moved some of the loose items to one side. Then he stepped inside and closed the door. One step forward then onto his knees, one crawl then half-roll onto his back, sit and draw the knees up. Lean his head against the underside of the staircase, his shoulder comfortably wedged in place.

The bare light bulb shone from high on the far wall. The house was silent and empty as far as he could consciously tell. Under here he could see everything at a glance. Whatever might be on the staircase or up in the bedrooms he was definitely alone in here. After a few moments he crawled towards the door and placed some paint tins and the hoover across it as a barricade. He then returned to his sitting position in the narrowing space at the back, gripped the golf club, and relaxed.

The Third Toilet and Joe

Joe asked his hostess 'Why do you have a toilet in there?' The hostess was a little taken aback, guests were not usually prone to criticise or question even the obvious failings of her new house. Not that the under-stair toilet was a design fault; it was very convenient and saved lots of climbing the stairs and all that. But Joe remained unconvinced. 'Where's the hoover then? What do you do with your coats? Don't you have two other toilets upstairs?'

'Joe the house is the house – what do you want from me? An apology? I didn't design the bloody thing.'

'I'm just curious why they put a toilet in there. There's even a frosted window which is completely useless under the stairs.'

'Well the toilet makes perfect sense because it's convenient. The window makes perfect sense because there is daylight in there so big clumsy idiots like you won't miss the toilet and piss all over my carpet.'

Joe paused before answering but subconsciously decided it was worth the social embarrassment of honesty. 'But it isn't convenient – it's too small to stand upright so I'm bound to spray piss all over the place. I'd say every man who goes in there is too busy leaning backwards and pushing his crotch towards the toilet to be too sure of what they're aiming at. You can't fit your head in over the bowl. I'd guess your carpet is drenched at this stage. I had to turn my head to one side just to fit in and I definitely had some spillage on the right side as I over-compensated. I think those toilets are intended for women, you know so you can back up to them and sit down. Or men taking a dump, though who'd want to in earshot of everyone in the living room?'

On all subsequent visits Joe was encouraged to use the upstairs bathroom. He couldn't help noticing through the open door that the hoover stood in the spare bedroom.

The Estate Agent and Joe

The estate agent was tall, svelte and drove a silver Audi – the lower-powered and cheaper version. Joe in his jeans hung back until most of the browsers had moved away, clutched the nasty cardboard brochure and pretended to examine the wall for damp. Tap the plaster lightly and see if it crumbles to the touch

– good way of spotting rampant damp according to the programme on the telly. Look along the wall to see if it's straight. Joe looked along the wall and it looked straight, though there seemed to be a bulge at the bottom. He pressed his cheek to the plaster, closed one eye and squinted. He tried to remember if there were missing slates on the roof but he couldn't. The wall felt cold to his cheek but was it damp?

The agent was impatient – could they leave now as he had another showing in ten minutes and he didn't want to be late. The traffic could be terrible at lunchtime and he had to lock up. Joe launched into his rehearsed script; mortgage approval, own property quick to sell, offer a little below the asking price, quick closing, solicitor ready. Nothing registered on the agent's face. The bugger expected to get twenty per cent over the asking price. 'Your own property isn't even on the market, sir,' he sneered, 'we couldn't possibly consider you a serious purchaser.'

Joe shrank into the varnished hardwood floor, nodded resignedly at the bastard's response and drifted towards the solid wood front door with feature skylight.

'Just a second,' the agent barked, 'here's my card – in case you ever want to sell your own property.'

The Morning After and Joe

Joe woke. Beside him in the bed, actually in his bed, naked and sleeping she was. She lay on her side, her shoulder uncovered and her shoulder blade pointing at him. He could see her hair on the pillow and in the gap between pillows. He could see her ear, some of her arm; when raised on his elbow even her face in profile and a little of her breast could be stared at. Joe lay gently down on his side. He was very close to her – so close he could feel her warmth, her body forming a 'C' to his 'E'. Under the duvet her naked back and her full bottom were close to him so when she farted he felt the temperature change and the slight pressure. He stiffened at the realisation, the very thought that he was naked and she was naked and any moment he could touch her and she wouldn't turn away or run away or disappear into a corner of his dream where he couldn't quite recapture her because some annoying memory of work intruded.

Of course she wouldn't run. Why would she – they'd had sex, she was clearly attracted to him. Well they'd not actually had sex but they'd drunkenly peeled off clothes and touched and stroked and kissed and all that. She would hardly wake and lose the rag at him. Joe was softening again but he liked his pun. What if she was pregnant or had VD? Did she have a boyfriend or even a husband? What if this was the start of a disaster?

She stirred a little – Joe tensed but she didn't wake. Any moment now this would be over or this would continue all morning. His confidence dithered and weakened.

She stirred a little more, woke, seemed unfazed by the strange surroundings, and miraculously, joyously she slid backwards across the inches of no-man's land between them. Her bottom touched him. She half turned her head and smiled languidly. He put a hand on her shoulder and kissed her back.

'You're certainly up and ready early,' she said, her hand reaching back to congratulate him.

Flat-Pack and Joe

There's a lot of crap talked about flat-pack, thought Joe. Screws, MDF, chipboard, a bit of veneer, a few handles and hinges and runners and screws and an allen key or two – nothing much to it. The instructions are fine. No Swedish or missing bits or any of the old comedian's staple complaints. This set of drawers is solid and nicely finished. Stand it up and it's nice and level and doesn't rock or move around, no problem with flexing. All the drawers open and close with a nice smooth action. The handles seem pretty secure so no worries about them falling off. All in all a very nice job. Even the gaps are fairly even and all the lines look good. A bit unfortunate that the screwdriver had nicked a little of the veneer off the right side but no one would notice it. Actually, thought Joe, I'll do a proper job and glue on the broken piece so it looks pretty much perfect.

Gluing veneer isn't as easy as it sounds. The stray piece was small, no more than an inch long and more or less triangular with jagged edges. And of course it was rather thin. Joe dug out the aging twin-tube superglue with mixer/applicator stick included, and mixed what looked like the perfect quantity of each on a cleanish surface. 'Apply to both surfaces' said the packet – no problem there except in holding the veneer with his finger nails while applying the glue with the encrusted applicator stick. More glue remained on the stick than reached the back of the veneer. Placing the veneer's glue-drenched side against the clammy chipboard of the cabinet and pressing gently Joe's tongue emerged from between pursed lips and his brow furrowed. It looked OK but there was a lot of glue oozing out around the veneer piece. Joe dabbed with a tissue, succeeding only in leaving bits of tissue stuck to the glue. He found a dry cloth and dabbed with it. The tissue paper came away but so did the veneer piece. In replacing it glue got on Joe's fingers and he struggled to get the veneer to stay with the cabinet rather than joining his finger. When he finally withdrew his fingers he had to adjust the alignment of the veneer with the tip of a screwdriver. It worked, more or less, but there was still too much stray glue. File it down later, he decided, secretly sure he never would.

The glue packet promised five minutes for complete and life-long adhesion. Fifteen minutes passed before Joe gently prodded the veneer. It held fast. He gently tried to lift one corner with the tip of the screwdriver. It held. Success! He used the screwdriver to chip away at a little excess and milky glue. The glue and veneer parted from the cabinet and dropped to the floor. Joe reflected at length upon the impossibility of glue.

The Next Cubicle and Joe

Joe made a point of choosing the last of the five cubicles. All of them empty as it happened but he hated to listen to the sound of someone going near to him. Best bet was to go to the last one, that way the next person in the door would go to the first. A three cubicle no-man's land was as little as he could stand. Worst kind of cubicles too – gaps top and bottom, no real privacy and definitely no sound-proofing. Joe had a problem taking a shit in public, didn't even like pissing at urinals in case he was over-looked. He liked to think that's what kept him out of the army. He settled into place, hovering a couple of inches above the seat. Nothing more repulsive than the thought of sitting where someone else's fleshy warm moist arse had been. As the stirring began he noted the sound of the first of the double doors to the toilet opening. This was never good – Joe preferred solitude in the entire room for a successful dump. Still, he thought, as long as whoever it is just stays as far away from me as possible.

The new man walked down the line of cubicles until he reached the one next to Joe and entered it. To his horror Joe heard the unmistakable door, belt, zipper, toilet-seat, first-wet-fart sequence that signalled another person taking a liquid dump within three feet of him. Separated only by a piece of plywood so flimsy it could fall over. While he couldn't yet detect the inevitable odour he could imagine it and sometimes for Joe imagining it was the worst part. He screamed 'Why the hell didn't you go into one of the other cubicles you fuckwit.' Screamed inwardly that is; it could be his boss next door.

His own evacuation ruined he pulled up underwear and trousers, tucked in his shirt, flushed the unused toilet, washed his unsoiled hands, threw a withering glance at the only closed door, winced at the sounds of another's turds slapping fetid water, and went to try another toilet.

The Plumber and Joe

The plumber emerged from behind the kitchen cupboard.

'I don't see too much trouble with this to tell you the truth; we could get the piping in the back and take a spur off the taps for the water and run the outflow back into the washing-machine pipe. Straightforward enough.'

Joe thought the plumber didn't look very plumberish. Where was his toolbelt or work shoes? The plumber's phone rang for the second time and he didn't apologise this time. Joe had been very understanding at the first call; he thought he was being polite but he'd really just revealed his weakness. He needed an incisive question.

'So with the shower and the dishwasher what am I looking at,' he asked weakly.

The plumber had already said fifty euro for the dishwasher piping and six hundred for the shower.

'Six hundred and fifty all in,' said the plumber as though he was talking to an old lady.

'And when could you do it?' asked Joe shakily.

'Well we're up to our tonsils and we have loads of jobs coming up. This is a handy job though, you'd do it in a day easily. I reckon I could get here by the end of the month. Tell you what, write down your number and I'll call you in a week to make a definite arrangement.' Joe wrote his name, number and then his address and 'dishwasher and power shower – €650' on a post-it. 'Two weeks,' he half-asked half-told the plumber.

'The two jobs done in a day by the end of this month for certain,' replied the plumber.

Joe shook the hand offered and knew that he'd never meet the man again.

The Hot Tub and Joe

'Good game.'

'It was, a great game. I like the way they really go for all-out attack, almost the Keeganish "We'll beat them five–four" sort of stuff. None of the dreary defensive crap you get with the other lot.'

Joe was comfortably sitting in a nice chair with a glass of beer. Maybe feeling a little bit gassy from the tinned beer, maybe just a little bit unsure what to do now the game was over, but comfortable all the same. Nice house this; Bob had done well. His wife was still very attractive too, though she'd gone out early on and wouldn't be back. Just Joe and Bob to watch football, drink a few beers and have a chat. It'd been years since they were on their own together. Didn't get together very much since Joe had moved to his house in the suburbs. Back in the old days there was women and lack of money and drinking sessions and all that for them to talk about. Things they read in the paper or something some idiot politician had said to laugh at. Bob liked a stupid politician as much as the next man but Joe thought he was getting a bit settled. Gone conservative over the years. He even went to mass these days – the fault of the wife probably.

'This really is a nice house,' said Joe, after a reasonable silence, turning his head theatrically to look around. 'Any plans to change it around or add anything?'

'No, we have pretty much everything we need in this place. Even the garden's a decent size, and the hot tub hasn't used up much of it despite what everyone said.'

Joe was intrigued. 'You have a hot tub? I've never even seen one – do you use it much?'

'It's great,' Bob replied, 'we only got it a few weeks ago but we're in it all the time. You don't even have to fill it – the water stays in there for a couple of weeks, then you can pump it out and fill it again.'

Joe didn't much like the sound of that – second-hand water didn't have the sexy feel he associated with a tub. A quick image of him, Bob and Bob's wife in the tub came to mind. Bob could be called away and his wife might suggest to Joe to stay on, why rush off just because Bob was going? Weren't they all friends for years?

'Come on,' said Bob, flushed with enthusiasm. 'We'll have a go in it. Bring your beer.'

Joe was horrified. 'I haven't got any sort of togs or anything with me,' he pointed out, feeling stupid even as he said it.

'You don't need togs for the love of god, we've known each other for years. Just drop your clothes and jump in. I'll go switch it on – follow me out.'

Bob went to the garden through the French doors and over the decking. Joe began considering several issues. First, he had been naked with Bob before, in communal showers after football and all that. Second, Bob was a married man and Joe a heterosexual – it was ridiculous to feel awkward just because you're naked with another man. Third, being naked in the tub made it easier to see how his fantasy with Bob's wife could work out better when she came home and jumped in with them, naked of course, and then Bob was called away. Fourth, hot tubs aren't all that big and it would be hard not to have some sort of contact with Bob, however innocuous. Fifth, Bob was an unattractive man and Joe didn't want to look at his naked body, not that he wanted to look at a good-looking man either of course. Sixth, the water was at least a couple of weeks old and who knew what kind of shite might be washing around in it. Seventh, how could he refuse. Eighth, what if he slipped climbing in and hit his nads on the side of the tub. Ninth, what if he had an erection from the fantasy about Bob's wife. Tenth, what if Bob's wife came home and thought they were weird to be naked in the hot tub and made it impossible for Joe's fantasy ever to come true. Eleventh, was he clean. Twelfth, was Bob clean. Thirteenth, would he be expected to do this every time he came round in future. Fourteenth, if Bob's wife forced him to go to mass she probably wouldn't be positively disposed towards jumping naked in the hot tub with her husband's friend.

Fifteenth, why hadn't Bob just bought a pool table like any normal person.

The Draper's Son
Jack Murray

I pressed the buzzer, and a large glass-panelled door opened onto a hallway with a narrow wooden staircase at one end – the type you'd see in a convent. In front of me was a sign indicating where each company was located in the building. I scanned it quickly until my eyes fixed on my destination – James G. Dillon and Sons – Solicitors and Commissioners of Oaths – suite 1, first floor.

As I walked up the steps, my stomach rumbled with childhood nerves. Before school exams, I used to get so nervous I could hardly function, hardly speak. My hands would clam up and the writer's dent on my index finger would sweat and ache like vinegar in a cut. I felt like that right now, but also self-aware. I could hear my lungs fill up my chest as the material in each trouser leg rubbed against the other with every upward step. My mind was racing with thoughts, yet blank. I wanted to be anywhere but here.

The office door was opposite the first flight of stairs. I entered a dimly lit ante-room and was greeted by a pleasant receptionist.

'Hello Sir, my name is Julie. Can I help you?'

'Hello, I'm Philip Kenny. I am here to see James Dillon, I have an appointment for 10.15.'

'He is expecting you; if you could take a seat, he will be with you in a moment.'

I sat into a leather arm chair which had seen better days, and waited for what seemed like an eternity. Why is it that waiting-room chairs throw up the most unusual sitting experiences? My arse was at the same level as my ankles and I nestled in vain to find comfort. To pass the time I fluctuated between pretending to read the old gossip magazines on the coffee table, and counting the patterns on the mouldy blue wallpaper, blurring and focusing, blurring and focusing.

After some time a door opened across the hall and a slight man in his late fifties appeared. He approach and extended his hand to me.

'Hello Philip, thank you for coming,' he said, ushering me into his office, which was dominated by an over-large desk and an obviously plastic plant which must have been at least six feet high. And like all solicitors James Dillon's desk was weighed down with stacks of mustard-coloured files, all in need of desperate attention.

We took a few moments to deal with the normal pleasantries before he got down to business.

'I know it can't be easy to deal with your father's last will and testament, but as you're his only child and closest living relative I would imagine it shouldn't take too long. I will begin.'

He opened the folder and began to read the will that my Dad had dictated to him.

'I, Peter Kenny, of the town of Ballinasloe, being of sound mind, memory and understanding, do make, publish and declare this writing to be my last will and testament; hereby revoking all wills and testamentary writings by me at any time heretofore made.

'First – I direct that as soon after my decease as conveniently can be, all my just debts and funeral expenses be fully paid and satisfied.

'Second – the matter of the family home and business, Kenny Man . . .'

In that split second my mind began to wander and that phrase stuck in my head. 'Second, the matter of the family home and business, Kenny Man . . .'

Kenny Man wasn't any ordinary business; it was the biggest men's and boys' drapery shop in all of east County Galway. It sold every possible item of clothing that any man or boy could ever want, from caps to cravats and ties to three-piece suits. It even specialised in cummerbunds and had a larger range of shoes than any other shoe shop in the town.

It was the size of two large hay sheds, laid out over two spacious floors, connected with a wide old staircase. The men's department was on the ground floor, boys' on the first floor.

It had one of the best locations of any shop in Ballinasloe, situated in a large three-storey building on Main Street, beside Sullivan's pub and directly across the street from Salmon's Department Store – one of the busiest shops in the town and a department store before Ballinasloe knew what a department store was.

My Dad, Peter Kenny, was the founder and proprietor, and if ever a man was born to sell men's clothes it was my Dad. Outwardly he was a fine balance of politeness and neatness, two qualities which made him an excellent salesman.

Inwardly, he was very determined – not so much a singular quality, but an ever-altering collage of facades. On the good days, he was single-minded and inspirational, a community leader and a business example. It is difficult thing to say about your father, but on the bad days, he wasn't any better than a pig: thick, rude, stubborn and generally quite impossible.

Dad was not a vain man, but my Mam used to say he was always 'exceptionally well turned out'. He figured he had no business advising his customers what to wear unless he dressed every day as if it were his last.

He was tall and slight with a physique that would make a jockey smile. No matter what he ate, and he ate plenty, it never registered on his slight frame. He had black shiny hair combed over to one side and fixed in place with a generous daub of hair wax. His shoes, always black patent with laces, shone like mirrors. The most expensive three-piece suit on offer in the shop was always on his back, and he had a particular weakness for Pierre Balmain.

He grew up in a small flat over my Granddad's sweet shop at the top of St Michael's Square. Even though he always said they hadn't room enough to swing a cat, he loved it. His room was only wide enough to fit a single bed while still being able to close the door. It was at the front of the building, and from that perch he could see the World.

To the left, St Michael's Church and the market square and to the right was the centre point of the town, where Main, Dunlo and Society Streets met. And if that was not enough, just outside the window was the Lazy Wall where the town's characters gathered every night to talk and drink. He often stayed up late, lying in his little room with the window open listening to drunken stories and fights.

In 1960 he passed his leaving certificate in Garbally College – the local boys' secondary school. That summer was spent working in the sweet shop, while his friends took jobs in the bank, teaching and the civil service. Not surprisingly he soon tired of selling quarts of bull's eyes and apple drops and made plans to go to London in September.

While all of his friends' ambitions were to work on London's building sites, Dad had a different idea of work. On his first day over he donned his best suit, got the tube to Knightsbridge and walked into the world-famous Harvey Nichols store, looked for the manager and asked for a job. The manager's response was burned forever in his brain.

'All right Paddy, you're a plucky sort and I like that. So we're going to take a chance on you, so don't let me down, son. Start Monday 7 a.m., report to the goods entrance. You're our new storeroom runner.'

Dad aimed to impress. He didn't want to spend his time there in the stores when all the real action was out on the shop floor. At twenty-two he became Harvey Nichols' youngest-ever Head of Shirt Sales. He dealt with all the wealthiest London businessmen and acted as a personal shopper for members of the royal family more than once, but he would never tell us which ones. I knew that really annoyed Mam, because she loved the royals.

He returned home knowing all he wanted to do was sell men's clothes, and in the spring of 1964 Kenny Man was open for business.

My Mam's family was originally from Ballyhaunis, County Mayo, and she came to Ballinasloe to train as a nurse. Her first encounter with Dad was in the Duggan Park during a Galway–Mayo football match. It was a crystal cold January day and Dad pushed his way into the crowded stand in search of a place to sit. The only remaining pew was amongst a very noisy group of Mayo supporters, but beside a very beautiful woman. Immediately he noticed that her striking red hair was almost as red as her Mayo flag and her warm, full cheeks.

They didn't speak at all, but shared a warm smile as he sat down. Despite the tension of being on opposite sides, he enjoyed being in her company – he could tell she was feisty and he liked that.

Towards the end of the game he broke the silence to ask if she would have time for tea in Hayden's Hotel before returning to Mayo. Her face lit up, she smiled and said she would love to go for tea and, if he liked, they could order a large pot and a bun, because she was training to be a nurse in Portiuncula Hospital and was not in a rush to go anywhere. The tea must have tasted very good, because they married in Rome that August after a whirlwind romance.

Romantic was not an adjective that you would use to describe my parents' relationship. You would probably even find it difficult to call them affectionate, but none the less they had what you might call a solid practical bond, the sort that unquestioning good friends have. He was dedicated to the business and she did her best to keep him and me happy.

Even though the Kenny Man was one of the most successful businesses in the town, my parents never lived in a large house befitting their wealth, because my Dad insisted on making the family home in his tiny bachelor flat over the shop. It was a very cramped living space, but it was home to him and he wouldn't tolerate any talk of moving out.

The largest room was the kitchen–living room, which was divided in two by a cream-coloured counter. White beauty board kissed the walls and the living area had space enough for two brown armchairs and a leather sofa – one of our few luxury items.

The kitchen had wooden cabinets made by Teddy Donovan, a local carpenter, in return for Dad dressing him on his wedding day. It had a large deep porcelain sink and narrow kitchen table with three chairs for family meals.

My parents had the double bedroom, which was only a double bedroom in name, qualifying as it was possible to fit a double bed, and not because it was particularly spacious.

In my room you had to face your arse to the door and reverse onto the bed. When I got a bit older I begged my Dad for more space; he eventually relented and came up with a very Japanese solution to my problem. I got one of those bunk beds where the bottom bunk has a desk and the top is the bed.

There was also a small bathroom, some attic space for storage, and my playroom which doubled as a clothes storeroom for the shop, with suits, ties, jumpers and shirts.

The flat was a melting pot of competing cooking and drapery smells. Sometimes it was a mix of boiling bacon and shoe polish or a mesmerising smell Mam just called 'newness', because it was the smell of the inside of a new car, new shoes or a new suit. She was convinced there were cans and cans of 'newness' in the manufacturing plants and new products were given a healthy spray before facing the world.

Even after I was born Dad insisted on continuing to live over the shop, much to the annoyance of my Mam.

'I don't care what you say, Mary, this is the best spot in town and isn't it our home? Can't you walk everywhere and everything is close?'

'But we have no back garden and there is nowhere for young Philip to play.'

'Who cares about a back garden? Can't the young lad go up into the fair green and kick a ball? If it was good enough for me, it'll be good enough for him.'

And that was always how the row ended with Dad getting the upper hand and Mam going silent. Moving out began as something that he was not inclined to discuss, and the more she pushed him, the more his resolve hardened, until it was obvious that leaving the tiny flat over Kenny Man was my Dad's Stalingrad. He didn't want to do it and that was it. So my Mam did not mention it and suffered on in silence.

As I grew from a baby to a boy, our lack of living space became more of a problem. My cot, play pen and pram could have done with a house all of their own. Mam resented having to put the pram in the shed at the back of the shop and carry me up three flights of stairs. And of course you always had to come through the shop to go upstairs, because there was no other way. It was bearable when I was quiet or asleep, but not when there were bits of food stuck to my bib or to Mam's hair.

She hated living in a goldfish bowl and made a promise to herself to do everything she could to offer me all the opportunities that life had to offer. She always imagined living in the country in a big house with stables and acres and acres of land to roam. Each Friday she did the shop's accounts for the week and saw the mounting balance, and Dad's insistence that he wasn't going to move from his perch over the shop. It depressed her.

'He'll be a great lad and he'll grow up to love this shop. I can see him here one day behind this till and I want to give him all that I had,' Dad used to say.

'Peter, you grew up over a sweet shop and you had nothing.'

'Exactly, and it didn't do me any harm, did it? And when we're with St Peter young Philip will probably live here and be happy.'

They fought often, at least once a day from what I can remember, and it was always either about the business or the flat. At first they were what you'd call band-aid fights that were easily overcome. Dad would sneak up behind Mam at the kitchen sink, give her a squeeze and a big kiss and everything would be OK. He even managed to buy flowers once or twice. But they continued to hurt each other like two people walking around in the dark until all the love was worn away and all that was left was anger and resentment.

As I grew up, broadening my horizons became my Mam's method of getting back at Dad by ensuring whatever I did it would not entail running a drapery shop in Ballinasloe.

If there was something new to be learned I'd be signed up for the classes. There were guitar lessons in the Emerald Ballroom, tin whistle classes in the Social Centre and piano practice in the convent, horse riding on Saturday mornings and boy scouts on Saturday afternoons. Not to mention hurling, football in the Duggan Park on Sundays and soccer in Curragh Park on Friday nights.

To counteract this, Dad insisted that I work at least an hour every weekday in the shop, as well as a full day Saturdays and all of my holidays. Like Mam's extra-circular activities it wasn't open to question. I was the ball in a game of marital tennis and when you live in a small apartment with demanding parents you become quite adept at doing almost anything to keep the peace.

Many hobbies came and went until one day Mam took me to the local swimming pool for a lesson. Once my toe hit the water I knew I was going to be good at it. After three lessons I was able to swim a length; after a month I won a competition in my first gala. Once my swimming obsession took hold, the time I devoted to the other pastimes reduced until they stopped altogether and I devoted myself to swimming.

At best, my Dad was indifferent to my interest and achievement in swimming. All he wanted was for me to finish school, serve my time in a drapery shop in Dublin for a couple of years, and return home to work with him in Kenny Man.

By my leaving cert year I had won four under-age national titles. Training, working and studying were putting a huge strain on me. Swimming training began at 6 a.m. each weekday morning. I would then rush home for breakfast before school. Once school was over I'd rush home and work for Dad until closing and then I had to do my homework before getting up at 6 a.m. to do it all over again. Pretty soon I was falling asleep at the desk in school and my school results were suffering. I kept pleading with Dad to let me off the shop work, but he wouldn't budge an inch. Telling me it would make a man out of me and that it hadn't done him any harm.

It was getting close to the time when I was going to have to decide what I wanted to do after my leaving certificate exams. My swimming coach told me if I wanted to study commerce in UCD he would ensure I got a sports scholarship on the strength of my swimming results, but I knew that Dad expected me to stay and take over the business.

Then one nondescript evening after the shop had closed for the night, the goldfish bowl of our living conditions reached a very inevitable and dark natural crescendo. What had been festering in the pressure cooker of my head for months exploded around a quiet kitchen table.

Mam was at the cooker frying rashers and potato cake for our tea. She made the most perfect potato cake with butter and salt mixed in perfect measure. Before cooking she opened a few doors to dissipate the strong smell that only the fusion of a frying pan and a rasher can create.

Earlier that morning Dad had received delivery of the latest range of Balmain suits and they were placed neatly for pricing in the storeroom next to the kitchen. Being caught up in the cooking process, Mam forgot to close the storeroom door and when Dad's shiny shoe lifted off the top stairs step into the living room he rushed instantly into a high rage.

At first he began by shouting and cursing.

'Didn't I fucking tell you never to cook and leave the door of the storeroom open? You have just fucking ruined thousands of pounds of new suits in there.'

He hurried to examine the extent of damage and returned even angrier than before.

'I knew it, they all fucking smell of grease and rashers now. How am I going to sell a wool suit with silk lining when it smells of fucking rasher? How fucking stupid are you?'

For a full five minutes Mam stood stoically, as if not listening, never looking up from the pan, and fiercely concentrating on the culinary state of the rashers. Then something quite unusual happened, after taking the abuse for twenty years she answered back.

'Fuck you, Peter. It's your fault for having us live in this fucking shoe box. You're so self-obsessed. It's inhuman to be cooped in a few rooms like this, especially when you have enough money to buy half the street.'

The bully was never answered back before, and when the initial shock wore off him, he did what had served him so well throughout the years, he attacked. Exploding in a rage, he kicked over a kitchen chair.

She stood her ground.

'Come on, Peter is that all you've got? I'm sure you've got a swing left in those boxer's arms – maybe one last punch in the stomach or a fist-full of my hair. Don't stop now just because Philip is here. Maybe you'd like to tell him about all those cheap bitches around the town you've been keeping going for years.'

In an instant he made a lunge across the table for Mam, first catching the side of her jumper, then grabbing and squeezing her throat with both his hands. She coughed and wheezed like a puppy on a leash. I had never noticed, until that moment, what large hands he had for a small man. I could see the delicate veins in her neck bulging to the point of explosion, as her rosy red cheeks were going blue.

Instinct is a strange thing. I had never laid an aggressive hand on my Dad before. Now, beating him to a pulp was my sole objective in life. I wrestled his shoulders from behind and managed with difficulty to drag him off Mam's tiny frame. He swung an elbow which winded me, and then a punch. I ducked and punched him as hard as I could between his legs.

As we watched him lying rolling on the ground I had made one of the biggest decisions in my life in an instant.

'You're a fucking animal. How could you do that? I should call the Guards. Then we'd see what a big man you are. Mr Retailer, Mr Shopkeeper. Everyone would see you for what you really are – a bully and a wife-beater. You can take your shop and shove it up your arse. I'm leaving here for good.'

My Mam and I packed our bags and left that night and we never lived in the flat above Kenny Man again. She moved back in with her sister in Ballyhaunis and got a job working in a local nursing home. I became a border for my final few months in Garbally before going to UCD.

After college I got a job with an accountancy firm in Dublin. That's where I met my wife, Amy. We're married now and we have two small boys. Jack is five and Bobby is three.

Mam moved to Dublin when I finished in college and got a job nursing in

St Vincent's and lived in a small apartment in Donnybrook. She thrived on having her own space. She worked hard for her new-found independence, but it was all to no end. She felt unwell one day and ignored it as a 'flu and by the time she was diagnosed with bone cancer it was too late. She survived three weeks.

Dad came to the funeral and it was the first time we met in ten years. He looked a grey reflection of himself, a decade of drinking and gambling had taken their toll. He shook my hand like an ordinary mourner and said 'I'm sorry for your trouble, son.' I thought that being such a stranger at the funeral of his own must have been some cross to bear.

As the years passed my anger towards my father mellowed and I visited him every now and then, mostly at Christmas time. He knew his grandchildren and that was as strong as the emotional connection went.

He died on his own, a very sad and sorry death. By the time the milkman saw the smoke coming out of the top window of the shop at 5 a.m. it was far too late to save him. The fireman said the only consolation was that the smoke would have got him way before the fire.

His charred remains were found slumped over the kitchen counter. The fire investigator said he had come back late from the pub, put on the chip pan and fallen asleep. The building was totally destroyed; nothing was left.

James Dillon read from the will . . .

'Second – the matter of the family home and business Kenny Man; I leave it to my only son, Philip.'

Cuckoo in Flight
Ian Mitchell

'Tell me about you,' you said last night, and I dodged the bullet. Tonight I'm trying again.

It seems to me that some of us live with a beginning we might never recapture. The distance from there to us is too vast to measure and even if we went back all we might find is disappointment.

We come so far on our journey before we even begin to walk. Seems like there's years and years of shaking the dice in the tumbler, waiting for that elusive six to come out and get us to the game. At least that's how it's been with me. If false starts were currency I'd be on easy street by now.

Of course to understand why I'm the way I am you need to know a little more about me. Pour yourself a coffee. This might take some time.

They say – that ubiquitous 'they' who manage to comment on everything, yet walk unrecognised along the pavements of our experience – they say that where we live out our first six months of life makes us who we are. Maybe that's true. Salmon believe it for sure.

My own journey began over half a century ago under a sun-blazed African sky. I was an Irish child, born miles from Ireland in Etinan village, southern Nigeria. No radio, no TV, no electricity, no telephones. There was no football, no jumpers for goal posts, no picking teams in the street. There weren't even streets. Just dusty pathways. And for six years this was my beginning. Where I belonged. With lizards in the bath. Home. My Dad built and practised in a hospital there in what was little more than a clearing in the jungle and my parents lived there till I was twelve.

Half of the kids I played with were starving, with bellies so round that at first I thought they were fat. Many of the others were maimed by leprosy, stump-limbed, truncated. Normality comes in so many shapes and guises – I guess it's really just another word for what we know best.

But, you know, it was the night time – the dark black, star studded, all-embracing night time – that was when dreams were born. Midnight leaning out of the window in the mud wall of home listening to the noises drifting up from the river, to the muffled jungle music of fifty-seven varieties of animals vying with the frenzied drumbeat of dancing Ekpo men in the village up the way, whispering secrets to the unclouded stars, enchanted by their mesmerising brightness; that was where they took their root.

And all of your long, long life you want to find them again.

Everyone's long, long journey begins under the heaven tree. Can you count stars, Abraham? Is that a cow I see jumping over the moon? There's magic brewing in that humid nightblue fruit – the magic that makes us urchins want to become someone, arrive somewhere, create, build, experience. To know.

And sometimes we want to be known.

I'm trying here to open up my soul and share with you the savage beauty of the place where I learned to walk and joyfully experiment with my first clumsy words. To introduce you to the woman that is life under the African heaven tree. She needs no youthful bloom for beauty; hers is a different kind of grace that age enhances and that time makes more striking. And I learned to be and become in the shelter of her cradling, and she has forever put her name on me and painted me with her mark. I still carry it.

Of course I knew her before the war. I knew her before the virus. I knew her before cynicism and opportunism corrupted her. I knew her when she had dreams.

And then I left. I'm to live with my Grandmother and Go To School. Six years old and already on the road. Discovering Ireland. Hoping to put down roots. Remembering. Longing. Six years of trying to work out where home might be. Some kind of human shuttlecock, bouncing between Africa and Ireland.

A kid with a suitcase.

'Hey, Ian, Ian, Ian, I have a chocolate bar for you. Fry's. Your favourite.' She's holding it out towards me, big welcoming smile on her face.

Port Harcourt airport. July 1st 1960. Blazing sun, eager faces meeting me. And I'm barrelling down the tarmac wrestling with my bags.

'I've been keeping this Fry's bar for you for ages. It's all for you.' Yes, and it's become a sticky melted mass in the heat of the sun, in the heat of your hands, in the heat of the moment. Kid sisters, can you believe them!?

It is as if I have stepped into another dimension. Taken in two days through the sky to a place so recognisably alien. The familiar unknown. It's a paradox all right.

Oh, and did I mention the smell? You can't describe it. You just remember. Africa. The never-to-be forgotten aroma of the always emerging continent that never ever quite emerges. Back. After twenty-four months. After twenty-five per cent of my life.

And I'm there for two months reliving and re-rooting. I'll never forget those months. Meeting old friends. Visiting favourite places. And most of all, just re-connecting and remembering. They were the best of times.

And then gone. Almost immediately it seems. Gone back to Belfast.

There is no heaven tree in Belfast. Not really. That was a time when we all had dreams. But somehow the clouds seemed to gather too quickly in the winter evenings and the darkness never seemed to dance and flicker like the darkness that I wanted it to be. There was no tapestry of nightblue black and dancing silver pinpoint to seduce me. No jungle sounds to inspire me. Even the rain was different.

And yet I am there. A world traveller. Doing my next stretch. Belfast. Streets for football. Kids with no bellies – though I must confess that my own belly grew fat on the food. On the Frys. Fry's bars. Fry-ups. But no lizards in the bath, no fifty-seven varieties of animals, no Ekpo men. No heaven tree.

And so by the River Lagan I sat down and wept. How could I sing my heart's song in such a strange land?

There are no chocolate bars next time I step off the plane in Port Harcourt. Though I'm sure there's going to be yam. Yam is wonderful. Oh and corn, fresh yellow corn on the cob. Not frozen. Not imported. Corn just picked this morning. And oranges that until just before breakfast grew on trees. Before the war there was fruit. Before the war was when I ate the oranges.

In the years I have been in Belfast I have purchased my treasure chest of memories and my fair share of confusion. I have grown fat and played the jester because I could not understand the game as it ought to be played there. In fact it turns out that I will always struggle with calories and cholesterol. I will always have a talent for seeing as funny all that ought to be serious.

You get the drift don't you? Can you read the time-etched lines that criss-cross my soul? Do you understand my dilemma? There's a disconnection in me that has its roots under the African heaven tree, woven together with my dreams. Dreams and disconnection. Weeds and flowers. An enemy has done this.

You see I think it's the not knowing that's the hardest. Not knowing where's 'here' and being able to differentiate it from 'there'. Not sure where exactly you're the stranger. Somehow always on the outside. Too fractured to fit. Too many places to try to call home. Too many journeys.

The plane touches down in Belfast. It's 1963 and life is preparing to change. Forty years from now we'll still be changing.

We tried so hard, my friends and me. We did what young believers do. We wrote poems and sang songs to the darkling sky. We laughed until the first smile of dawn. We made time, we made music, we made commitments, we made love (not war – well, we were Boomers after all), we made babies, we made plans, we made communities, we made money, we made excuses. Until bloody Sunday after Bloody Sunday we saw our dreams ooze out their life blood and die.

Displaced and dreaming
Eyes on some far horizon
Scouring out meaning

No there was no heaven tree in Belfast. Not then. Not even now. Not really. There is simply entrenchment, spin and forms of words. There is memory and suppressed pain. We are all in the gutter, but the stars are out of sight. Maybe it's the fear. The fear of together; the fear of the then; the fear of the if; the fear of alone; the fear of forgiving; the fear of jumping first. What we have we hold. Till our day comes.

Belfast. It can do your head in.

Adulthood deconstructs hope. Being grown up, I have found, is about balance, about rationalising disappointment, about taking pleasure in small wins. Adulthood seems to take hope and confront it with evidence. But then sometimes, for maybe just a moment, something happens and we manage to shake loose from the constraints of being adult. Maybe we catch a momentary glimpse of how we might be, of the way the molecules we call 'us' might take flight and become beautiful – or maybe it's just because we're afraid of the alternative. Whatever it is, sometimes hope will just not lie down to die.

Of course, the thing is, sometimes we don't realise who we've become. Don't know that all those little momentary incidents, all those half smiles and lovers' kisses and private memories that we cling onto for meaning have all been slightly rearranged in our heads simply because we got older. Or because we let time or circumstance reorganise them in some arbitrary manner. Before we know it, all the jigsaw pieces that are us have been subtly moved to create a picture that we never ever imagined could be. Life's devious. It only takes a tiny shuffling.

And then one day we look in the mirror and wonder how we ever became who we became. Where those lines came from. How it was we made so many compromises. And maybe it disturbs us so much that we begin to swim back up the stream. Just like the salmon. Looking for home.

There are broken seat belts on this plane. They come off in your hand. Never travel on an airline with a Z in the name. My friend Oliver tries to complain. He fails. Nevertheless I am excited. Full of anticipation. I am On The Way.

Oliver thinks he might have grown up in the same village as the chief steward. He recognises the face, he says. He complains again. He was wrong.

In the small stifling airport they take our passports. They are carrying guns. There is insurrection in the air. Apparently the land is dying. War is now a lifestyle.

But that's not the point.

The point is (I told you about the smell, didn't I?) the point is that as I walked down the rickety, Z-in-the-name staircase, past the desultory piles of luggage on the tarmac (the landing staff are on strike), I smelled the smell. The never-to-be-forgotten aroma of the always emerging continent that never ever quite emerges. How did I live without it?

The point is that even in this fifteen-foot-square oven, with no passport and surrounded by hard, cold eyes toting guns I can almost see starlight. I can almost hear the night sounds, the muffled jungle music of fifty-seven varieties of animals vying with the frenzied drumbeat of dancing Ekpo men. I'm sure I saw a dream of mine glide by.

The point is that I'm back. Back in Africa.

The emerging never quite happened and the marks of failure are everywhere. There's a shabbiness now. Though I notice that the politicians are sleek and well groomed. Mostly in Armani. That happened in Belfast too, you know. There are shiny black Mercedes in cavalcades and status-symbol hotel buildings seeking to divert attention from the tragic.

Needing to escape the city we board a lorry. A lorry going anywhere. People piled high on the back. Hanging on by their fingernails. Singing. All around us the land lies wasting. There are few crops in the fields.

The virus has decimated the population. I see the children. The mothers. I know the statistics. This is the weapon of mass destruction that the willing will ignore. Sometimes problems are too complex.

Incredibly the children have not stopped laughing. Though their bodies are more wasted than ever. Many with limbs moulded into little prosthetic replacements. Because of the mines. Leprosy traded for landmines. Normality comes in so many shapes and guises – I guess it's really just another word for what we know best.

That night the sun sets vibrant orange over the tops of the palm trees and we sleep beneath the stars. One of the guys finds a black mamba in his sleeping bag. He beats it to death.

And so for a flake of my grown-up life I find myself back listening to the sounds in the dark black, light-studded, all-embracing night time. Nearer this time; no walls, mud or otherwise hemming me in. Listening to the sounds, smelling the smell, trying to count the stars. There's an elephant walking by our campsite. I huddle in my semi-sleep awe-struck. Under my own heaven tree. Though I am conscious that my companions have not even stirred. Is this where I belong? Home? Maybe. I am unsure.

A few weeks later I am gone. Back on the Z-in-the-name plane. I am displaced inside again. Gone back to Belfast. Home to mother Ireland. Home?

Your coffee will by now be drunk or cold. Here, hours have passed. It is almost dawn and I have tried to paint you my soul. Told you about me, like you asked. And once again, it seems, I have encountered my own questioning. My wondering. Maybe you understand, now you've read my meanderings. Feels like I'm always wondering, these days – the disjointing's buried itself deep. And here's the nub of what I'm wondering. The core. Just this. Is there ever a right nest for cuckoos?

Blue Light Loves
Emily Maher

Sadie stared at the blinking blue lights across the bay. Four of them, winking two by two in constant unison. Sadie found this comforting, repeated moments of sameness in the ever-changing city. She closed her eyes but the blue lights were still there behind her eyelids – blinking on and off forever.

Sitting on Sandymount Strand, with her back to a low wall; she had spread her coat roughly on the ground because the sand was wet and sludgy. Not her good coat; an old one she hardly wore, so it wouldn't matter that now it would be ruined.

This view was worth it though, she thought to herself. And smiled. She'd always have this view to savour. The Pigeon House from the far side of Dublin Bay, as the punctured morning sky lights up for the day. Flashes of neon streaking across the clouds. A seagull in silhouette. Always have this memory. Memories like this were special, things to be minded, taken care of, wrapped tightly in cotton wool and secreted away in a silken drawstring bag. Special like her and Martin.

Sadie fingered the ring, twisted it round and round. Let the stone glint and refract the light. It was almost blinding. Felt how sharp the six little prongs were. Once she had pushed it into the side of her finger and the scar had remained for more than a week.

'You could do damage with that rock,' Martin had said as they left the shop, a glint of mischief dancing in his eyes. And Fifth Avenue lighting up for the evening behind him looked unreal to Sadie. Like a scene from a film. They walked back to the hotel as if the city was theirs alone, although it was the busiest shopping day of the year. Nothing could invade their private world that night. The ring had been fitted.

'*A classic setting – we've been selling that for over a hundred years.*' Sadie smiled to herself as she remembered the day. Three months ago now and still as clear. Every syllable, every face in the crowd, everything so special. The magnitude of the happiness. The dodgy phone cards that conspired to keep their news secret. Martin at once restless and decided, nervous and bold.

*   *   *   *   *

Boldness was not usually an option for Sadie, who grew up afraid of her own shadow. A little mouse of a person scuttling from one heart-attack experience to another. Sadiemouse, her father used to call her, my little Sadiemouse.

She slept with the light on because she hated flicking the switch at the door. The journey from there to the bed was fraught with danger. Sadie was not fond of stories like 'The Three Billy Goats Gruff' and although she wasn't a religious child, she had conjured up an image of the devil with red horns and a flicking tail and tortured herself with the notion that he lived under the bed. Convinced herself that one day he'd catch her leg as she swung it from the floor. He would brutally drag her under, into the darkness, and slowly eat her alive. She thought, also, that there were robbers hiding in the bath when she went to brush her teeth, ready to pounce and drag a defenceless child off to their lair. Sadie was a mouse.

One day, When Sadie was about eight or nine her father came home with a box for her. A present. A blue light for beside her bed. No more devils; now she could leave it switched on for the journey from door to bed. They christened it 'Blue Light Day' and marked the date in her diary and on the calendar hanging in the kitchen with a bright blue marker pen from her art set.

'Now Sadiemouse will be safe for ever,' he said and kissed her on the nose. 'Goodnight Sadiemouse. Sleep tight and don't let the bed bugs bite.'

But one blue light for beside her bed didn't really help Sadie; it wasn't enough to make her tough. She needed something more than that. Something that would keep the bedbugs outside in the garden shed where they belonged. Sadiemouse wrapped the duvet round her legs, closed her eyes and tried not to think about the army of bedbugs marching across the carpet.

*   *   *   *   *

Sadie remembered the day she'd seen him for the first time. A fresh March day, windy but dry. She'd walked to the office to clear her head, thirty minutes of brisk stomping. A slightly different route than the one she normally took, just for a change. A sudden desire for a sugar fix had drawn her to this nondescript branch of a popular chain of convenience stores. The McDonaldisation of the newsagents, she thought to herself as the doors slid open, smooth as creamy milk.

There he was, standing behind the counter, his large flat hands spread across the pile of that morning's papers, king of the corner shop. He looked a bit strange, his grey suit casting him as a silent movie star, out of place in the garish Technicolour of the shop fittings and ready-meal displays. He must be the manager, Sadie thought. A cheeky smile flittering between his lips and eyes. They were friends from then, although neither knew it consciously; best friends.

Martin Russell, his badge announced alongside the cheerful dancing logo. Sadie didn't know then that this chance meeting was to mean the path of her life was irreversibly altered. All she knew was she'd have to go back. To see him again. To see his smile. The smile in his eyes.

And so it was for the next few weeks. A hurried fix in the morning and back again in the evening, ostensibly to grab a bar of chocolate or packet of crisps for the journey home, but really to see him once more. And even if he wasn't there, it was worth the detour on the chance he was.

Sadie always hoped Martin would be serving so she could look at his eyes, peek from the magazine display or take a sip from behind the coffee machine. Azure blue and piercing, they seemed to understand her solitary self better than anyone although their exchanges tended towards the monosyllabic. She'd spend hours sitting at her desk dreaming of her opening line for that evening.

'Busy day?' she might nonchalantly comment as she plucked an apple from the wire stand.

More often than not, she said nothing more than a whispered 'Thanks' as she brushed his chubby fingers to retrieve her pennies. An isolated moment of contact in her empty days and emptier evenings. Sometimes he stacked shelves and one of the other staff members stood behind the counter. Sadie hated those days.

* * * * *

In the distance, the blue lights were fading. The light was brighter now and it was harder to make them out across the bay. Sadie stood up and shook her coat. Her phone buzzed in the pocket of her bag and she knew instinctively it would be Martin wondering where she was. She climbed up the steps to the path and started walking towards the street.

'I'm just leaving now . . . I'll be home right away . . . I love you too.'

Sadie snapped her phone shut and put her hands in her pockets. A prong snagged the thin lining. You could do damage . . .

Martin would be waiting at home with the kettle just off the boil and a teabag in a mug for her. He was so thoughtful like that. Turning the bed down each night and filling her hot water bottle three-quarters full so there was no chance of it exploding. Death by scalding was a recent fear of Sadie's.

Sadie wasn't sure how she'd been so fortunate. Little Sadie, the mouse who had her first chaste kiss at seventeen and a half. No tongues, holding hands, an audience of peers. Leaving Cert night outside Flicker nightclub. She'd thought that was love for a few weeks. A couple of idle dreams and a strange sense of inexplicable anticipation. But Jason had turned out to be pompous and self-centred. And then nothing till the next one, longer, three months if she was remembering correctly. But she got bored with him too, and the next and the next and the next till infinity. Plus one. By twenty-eight, her friends were all engaged or married or pregnant and shacked up. Or had declared themselves bachelorettes for life – such a silly word, bachelorettes, a bit like those dancing Rockettes they'd seen last week.

'You could do that, love, if you wanted. You've got the legs, for sure,' and he squeezed her forearm playfully.

'Yeah, I can just see myself, high-kicking and perma-smiling.'

Sadie punched Martin lightly in the stomach and kissed his nose. Shorthand for I love you, you silly fool. Big hug.

Doesn't every relationship have its own language? The accumulated glances and subtle phrases that seem to define the space it occupies for its passengers. Sadie and Martin were learning that their own shorthand was rich and poor together, simple and complex, all at once a thing to declare to the world yet equally a tiny chicken egg to be cupped in warm hands and wrapped in soft golden straw.

'Welcome to Tiffany's. Which floor would you like to visit today?'

The lift attendant was dressed for a black-tie dinner dance and Sadie had never felt so scruffy in her life. Jeans and flat walking shoes. Messy hair from the wind and the open carriage. At least her jacket was fairly smart. But shoes make the difference. These people would see right through her, Sadie thought, and looked down at the swirly carpet on the floor of the lift. Martin put his finger under her chin, where the buttercups used to shine, and nudged her face to his.

'Second Floor. Wedding bands and engagement rings.'

Sadie jumped and Martin pulled away from the kiss and grabbed her hand in his. Small in large. Pulled her out of the lift and there they were. First time in Tiffany's, hell, first time in New York and she was about to pick her engagement ring. It was too perfect a thought for Sadie to have ever dreamed it, so she hadn't. Not even while she watched Holly eat her pastry and sip her coffee for the thousandth time, curled up on the sofa with the curtains pulled to shut out the world. Sadie wanted a happy ending, just like the film, but she didn't dare admit it to herself in case it didn't happen. She never thought she would be walking through Tiffany's, even if it wasn't breakfast time.

'Now are you glad I asked you to that shindig last year? Did you think then you'd be an old engaged woman in twelve months?'

She hadn't. Had never allowed herself to hope too high lest she'd fall from a personal Everest. Keep quiet, mind your dreams, say nothing.

It had always been the smile. The devilish, never-know-what-he-might-do-next, clown-on-a-tightrope-about-to-tumble smile. Unpredictable.

They walked around the glass cases and pointed at the rings, bejewelled, magpie heaven.

'Bling bling bling bling bling!'

Sadie mimed a teacher, finger on lips. Martin looked momentarily chastised but all of a sudden the smile was back and he pulled Sadie into a seat in front of one of the glass cabinets.

'We'd like to see some engagement rings, please.' His voice carried across the room. He took a piece of paper from his wallet and showed it to the sales advisor. She nodded and glided towards an anteroom in a corner.

'Martin, are you sure you can aff–' but Martin repeated the finger-on-lips gesture and Sadie's question trailed off into the shared ether of the day. The perfect day. Their day.

*　　*　　*　　*　　*

Sadie slid the lipstick across her mouth, clicked the lid shut and flung it into her bag. Her feet barely touched the ground as she ran down the narrow stairs. In the doorway stood a broad monkey, a smile bridging his open face.

'Right so, the taxi's waiting. I got you something – here.' Martin held out a tiny package.

He smiled that smile and Sadie knew that she'd always remember the first time she saw him, in the shop at the foot of the Pigeon House. The shop below the blue lights. The shop that gave Martin to her.

She slipped on her coat and placed her hand out to receive the little jewelled casket. She opened it slowly and her eyes lit up.

She opened the tiny blue box, her face alight.

'Earrings. To match your ring.' Martin held out his flat palm to grasp Sadie's. 'Happy anniversary, love. It's been a great year.'

Sadie took the box and stood beside Martin. She kissed his nose. I love you, you silly fool. Big hug.

Chance Photo of Three Coming Home
Lisa Allen

Our heads turned to the camera as ripe
berries to the sun - gleaming vigour -
or if you prefer - rabbits in headlights;
flash stares, reflects three ricocheted sniggers.

Chance man (we dubbed him Rasputin) closed in,
stood behind us - whole boat trip back we found
him, crowned him, in mirth. He snapped us
 - smiles forever frozen -
sunburnt and swollen with laughing aloud.

Arms slung low and wide - I remember the casual caress
of this stranger's shoulder: watch him mould himself
to our photo, sidling whiskered into our midst.
Eyes away in some other place,
his roughened hands gripped our waists.

Puckering performance simulates warmth
- he guzzles shards of raucous bliss.

Blanket of Bone
Lisa Allen

Hands crack and part ways,
Hands once glazed by youth's fray; the warmth of another day;
pale, slender, bright as milk stains on varnished wood
or tarnished by the sun, ruddy with the breath of a summer
just gone.

Hands pass over days and times,
familiar objects seem strangely denied
yet new ones stare unblinking back.

These hands have scratched and played
roamed through days, touched surfaces coarse and greyed.
They've felt velvet petals, rust-tinged metal,
cloth and coppers, skin and silent rage.

Uncaged by age or weather's pain, each morning
I turn my palms upwards to feel for frost or rain:
Small vibrations. The cotton train of my duvet
lifts itself away
and these hands feel for the wakeful cup of tea,
house keys -
Ways to unpeel mind from dreams.

Into a womb of clay one day
- I will look to your hands.
Hands once gloved by youth's stare; the warmth of another pair;

pain blankets your bones.
Faithless sinews.
These hands caressed children; they have woven themselves into earth.

I try to press youth into your scrawny hands.
I squeeze and knead the palms.

I try to tell you that it's mind over matter,
as I caress your beautiful broken hands.

Deserted Circus
Lisa Allen

Rotting walls chunk yellow light under brooding November skies
The gravely jest of path beneath the blackened mass
makes me dream of home.

Light sucked into feasting clouds
hints at a lone mast

A raw-boned tent stripped of tarpaulin
a vanishing big top.

Paraded laughter, shrieks and fawning
are swallowed whole by the shuffling wind;

Wind rasps across this barren stage
aping human laughter played and replayed
for entertainment's sake.

No electric human flesh to juggernaut
across the solid mass of earth.

A grey as nothing dirt path is random as the sky
that slits and thins to match its movement.

Night collapses over and over,
on building shells, a rotting fence;

There are no jugglers here -
snarling tigers, games or prizes

Just horizon's unseen dent.

Phantom Without Need of Ceremony
Lisa Allen

Its funny - for years all I knew of you related to me.
Forceful flashes gleaned from memory suddenly
don't suffice. Like eggshells tinkling shatter
cracking under spoon's first strike,
Fragile moments drown in chatter's daily strife.

When you laugh with me, it means so much to me,
Raises me above the roaring melee.
Tenderness can manifest itself in a smile or glance
- some favour eulogies, others quiet deeds
that leave stomachs howling or clothes askance.

And as I pour myself some strong, black coffee
- wrenched from bed to face the snoring tide,
I watch the milk swirl concentrically
- it blends as you sit down with me.

Phantom Without Need of Ceremony
I have left your house.
Your head is barer now but I remember
when it spun on periscopes to foil the drop,
the sheer cliff edge upon which every girl-child walks.

For many years I thought that every man
bearded and moustached,
could fill vacuums up with melodies
and slice the strings of neon's grasp.

So when I'm holding breath against my will,
Bunched fiercely into memory,
I see a young man hacking back the night,
Laughing at circumstance

And all that you have given me
You will never see - you're too natural for that
The cracked curve of your ever - giving eyes touches me
You arrest, amuse me.

I blink and you are vapour.

I tip my ashes, drain the slops.
I turn the key in doors of rented flats.

Now tumbling foot-brave upon the morning's poise
I crunch cries of wind and smog
with your song in my lightened limbs. Before long,
scraping beeping things will noose your car

You - gridlocked somewhere,
I - in my air-conditioned vault.

The Chance of My Life
Ian Mitchell

'Chance would be a fine thing,' laughed Bill O'Sullivan when Ruby told him he was having a son, 'sure all you can produce is daughters. You and your mother before you.'

And he was right. Between them Ruby and her mother had produced six girls. And no boys at all. Bill knew there was no chance.

'I'm telling you,' his wife replied with conviction. 'Me bump's a different shape and Molly can tell the sex from the shape of the bump. She's always on the money. Never been wrong yet.'

'Go on with you,' Bill repeated, 'Like I say, chance would be a fine thing.' And he kept saying it every time Molly appeared at the house making her predictions, until six months later his son was born. Seven pounds twelve ounces. Full head of coal-black hair. Eyes just like his father's. Chance O'Sullivan. There was nothing else they could have called him.

I'm George Armstrong, by the way. My part in all this is a small one but I like to feel it's significant. You see I've known him from back when we were at primary school, and I've been with him for the whole cresta run – well, except for the five-year experiment of course, he was on his own for that one. But, hey, I'm already getting ahead of myself and I need to start from the beginning. As I say, I'm George Armstrong. I'm fifty-two years old. Wealthy by most people's standards. Happy by anyone's. And I owe all of my wealth and a lot of my happiness to him. You could say he gave me the chance of my life.

I'd always wondered how he got his name. I mean, Chance, strange name for a guy. And he'd always been pretty close-mouthed about it. Then one night, around the start of the *Your Big Chance* reality TV show we were out in a Chinese restaurant in Leeds. We'd been auditioning the hopeful. Anyone who's ever eaten in Leeds knows the place, just round from the Yorkshire Post. Anyway, we had the banquet for two, crispy duck, the lot. And after a couple of bottles of wine he just opened up and told me. 'Tell it after it's all over, George, will you. Tell the whole crazy thing.'

The O'Sullivans lived in Westland Bungalows – a weather-beaten estate of tin Nissen huts towards the foot of the Cavehill Road, on the north side of Belfast. Chance was the third in a line of four children, the only boy. His parents spoiled him stupid as was the way back in the fifties when a son and heir was born.

Bill, his father, was a self-employed bricklayer, grabbing whatever sub-contract work he could from the old money-building families that ran the city construction scene. It would be another generation before the hungry young property developers would come with their cranes and change the Belfast skyline. Bill and Ruby had saved for years to try and scrape up enough money to leave Westland Bungalows and purchase one of the new semi-detached houses going up in Kylemore Avenue, or some such place further up the Cavehill Road. Sadly it seemed that every time they almost made it, the work would dry up or some family emergency would arise and their little pot of savings would be depleted. They had almost given up.

Chance made up his mind early on that he wasn't going into his Da's line of work. He'd looked at his father's callused hands and made his decision. Seen too many weeks with no pay cheque. Known too often the disappointment of cancelled holidays. Felt too keenly the social gap between himself and many of the other children at Cavehill Primary School. Heard the names they called him behind his back. *Chancey old Smellyman* and the like. No, Chance had another plan entirely. He was going to make an impact. And if he had to cut a few corners on the way, well that would be fine by him.

By age ten he was running a pitch-and-toss racket on the school playground. That's when he and I got together. I was from Sunningdale Park at the top of the Cavehill Road. I joined the school late, having just moved from Armagh due to my father's being appointed vice-principal. Chance and I had been kept behind for 'disrupting the class' on my second day, and a lifetime's friendship was born. We ran the scam together for two years – made a fortune. Man, those primary-five kids were so gullible. We took them for all that they had. The rules were simple. As many of you as liked stood in a big circle and tossed your coins. Thruppence got you into the game. If on any one throw there was an odd man out, that guy won the pile.

Now you'd be thinking there was no way at all to rig this. But Chance and I had a system. It had come to Chance one day when Mrs McWilliams was trying to explain about long division.

'If I just touched my head,' he thought, 'George could flip his coin to heads. And my shoulder if he needs to get tails.'

He had no qualms at all about the deception. 'Business is business,' he told himself, briskly.

He explained it well and I caught on fast. A bit of refining to make sure that sometimes, if there was no danger of losing the round, we both landed the same side of the coin. But on around seven flips out of ten Chance would give the nod. I'd worked out a way of checking my coin and flipping it over as I took my hand away. Totally subtle and unobserved. The thruppences would change hands. Another bunch of suckers suckered.

And, as Chance would say, 'Bob's your uncle.'

Or in this case Martin. An uncle of mine worked in a local branch of Barney Eastwood's betting empire. Never made it quite to manager, but knew all there was to know about odds, horses, and taking the punters. And even though his young devotee felt that he lacked ambition, Uncle Martin became, for a while at least, a role model to Chance O'Sullivan.

Martin would allow Chance, quite illegally mind, to stand beside him on a

Saturday and watch him take the bets. Learn the ropes. Chance was amazed at the way they kept coming. There really was one born every minute. He decided that his previous careful cheating was, in fact, unnecessary because the odds were so stacked against the punters – though he didn't suggest giving the thruppences back! And he wanted to learn everything.

Uncle Martin was amazed at the way Chance wanted to find out every single detail.

'It's as if the lad's found his vocation,' he would often say.

And sure enough, by the time he was sixteen he was expelled from the local high school for running an illegal betting operation out of the tuck shop. Earned himself a headline slot on the UTV News at Six. Chance didn't care. He was on the rise. Educated in all that mattered. (Though he did take three years out to hang around the student union in Rupert Stanley College, Belfast, making contacts and experimenting with some illegal chemical substances.)

You see, something had taken root in Chance O'Sullivan. It wasn't that he was a crook. And he certainly wasn't a conman (well except for the primary school playground incident, of course). No, it was more that he had a vision. Chance had a vision for alleviating the ordinariness of life. His own life and the lives of those around him. He had weighed up the world of his father and found it to be lacking. He wanted so much more out of life than his parents had experienced. And something inside him knew that he had been born at the right time.

The late nineteen-sixties and early seventies were an exciting time for Chance, and for so many of his peers. It was a world where the unexpected happened. Where miracles took place. Where the only rule was that life is unpredictable. Where there was magic in the music, in the new boutiques springing up all over Belfast despite the developing 'troubles', on the radio. Everywhere. It was working all around him. He wanted it to work for him.

He worked for a while in record shops and as a roadie for Strupp, one of the so-called intellectual bands that came out of Northern Ireland in the mid-seventies. He researched the music scene in Liverpool and London. He spent six months in Paris. I went with him on some of his trips and was amazed by his work rate. And his play rate. It was never dull hanging with Chance.

And all the while he was preparing for what he would do next. He knew there was a market for something in Belfast. Just what that might be took him a while to work out, but by eighty-two he had seen the vision for combining all his interests into one magnificent venture.

To create it he had to plough in most of his savings. Or at least, about £12,000 of them anyway, he told me. There hadn't yet been even a sniff of a ceasefire in Belfast, and the nightlife hadn't developed to anything near what it is today. So there were a lot of punters for his Take a Chance on Love musical roadshow extravaganza. For years it was all the rage at schools, scout halls and youth clubs. He even got a couple of one-off gigs at the student unions as part of rag week. Those were great nights. The punters loved his sideline book on 'Will they get it on tonight?' And he showed quite a talent for working out the odds correctly. Though he did know that there was a bit of cheating going on out there on the dance floor.

'You have to give the punters something, sometimes,' he would often say to me in his more reflective moments. 'Everybody's looking to feel superior, and it brings them back for more. And anyway, it all helps to create the illusion. To give them the magic.'

Chance's big break came when he read The Diceman – Luke Rinehart's nineteen-seventies book about a man who hands the course of his whole life over to the throws of a dice. Makes every decision according to the numbers that come up.

Now just about everyone born after nineteen-fifty has read Diceman at some stage of his or her life and a reasonable percentage of readers has even tried it on for an hour or two. Though not many dare to embrace the frightening chasm that opens up when the predictability of life is gone. I guess we're all control freaks under our own hats. But Chance was different. He felt, by the very nature of his name, and, I suppose, because of the growing vision in his soul, that he was called to it. You could say he felt it in his bones. It was, as Uncle Martin might have said, his vocation.

Starting towards the end of eighty-nine, Chance O'Sullivan gave more than five years of his life to being a Diceman. Lived everything by the rule of the dice. Every decision. Every relationship. The outcome of every journey he took was dictated by the fall of the numbers. Maybe he was having an early mid-life crisis – well, he was thirty-seven after all – or maybe the boredom of his life was just getting too much for him. I don't know. He told me, however, that he saw it as one long journey of self discovery. One long experiment to find out if he was lucky. And Chance was one lucky guy!

I didn't see him at all for those five years. It seems my number never came up. I didn't hear from him either, so the only information I know about those times is what Chance later told me himself. However I don't think he ever lied, misled or exaggerated about that time. He knew he had done something special. There was no need to spin.

At the end of his first five years he took stock. His stock looked good and by now he was quite the prosperous man about town. His current account stood at the princely sum of £67,000. He had shares and bonds to the value of £453,000 and was part-owner of a highly successful racehorse. He had made a substantial down payment on a home in middle-class Holywood, County Down with the proceeds of Take a Chance on Love (sold, I believe, at the dictate of a number four), and was easily making the small residual mortgage payments. He had travelled to every continent, had lived for six months in Florence, and had studied with monks on a Tibetan mountain top. He owned a villa in Tunisia.

He had learned to appreciate the opera, discovered spas and fine cognac and become a committed vegetarian. He sported a pony tail and dressed in black Armani. His life had certainly changed. For the better, he felt. And, to the best of his knowledge, he had fathered no children. Though he had been both married and divorced. (On numbers three and six, as he recalled.) Indeed, the experiment had produced magic beyond his wildest dreams. His life was unpredictably magnificent. Chance O'Sullivan was riding high. And if, deep in his heart, he had questions about what this dice life was producing in his soul, he hid them well. He just knew that something very special was directing his life.

It was early nineteen-ninety-five that he quit the dice. Feeling pretty confident that number one could not possibly come up for the sixth time on the bounce, he gave it the option 'Quit the dice'. He'd been spicing his life up with the 'Quit the dice' option on and off for a couple of months, but the option had never landed. His percentage game, he thought, was still in good shape. Freud or one of those guys would have had a lot to say about his inclusion of the option in the first place. It's a strange place, the old subconscious, and whilst the walls he had build up around his inner self seemed pretty secure both to himself and to those who felt that they knew him, there must have been some part of him somewhere that hungered for predictability. For what the rest of us call normality.

For a while after he quit he just didn't know what to do with himself.

'I was just empty, George. Washed out.' he said to me when he called me, later, to offer me a job.

It's like that for all of us, I think, if we walk away from all that we've come to know. And for Chance life with the dice had grown, in a paradoxical way, to feel so secure. He was self-aware enough to understand this, and to know that it was an illusion; but then again, he hadn't had to take responsibility for any of his own decisions since October seventeenth, nineteen-eighty-nine. His whole sense of personal accountability had been eroded. He had been subject to a higher power. Only obeying orders. For a few weeks his mind was paralysed. He became indecisive. Later he called it his deprogramming.

Chance being Chance however, it didn't take too long for his brain to kick back into gear.

'It just came to me,' was how he put it.

One day he was sitting in a little coffee shop in Botanic Avenue watching the students go by and he remembered the old days of doing the roadshow in the student union. It was just around ceasefire time too, and there was this whole sense of expectancy in the air. Just the atmosphere in which an entrepreneur of his experience might thrive. He just had to do it this time without the dice. Well, without using them himself anyway. The possibilities set him wondering.

A year later he opened the first of his *Chance Behaviour* clubs in Shaftesbury Square, Belfast. The city had seen nothing like it. Nowhere had seen anything like it. By the end of ninety-seven there were five of them. One in Belfast, one in Temple Bar, Dublin, and more in Manchester, Newcastle and Soho. He had plans for a European franchise.

It was a simple idea really. For a moderate entrance fee (£50) patrons were given a pair of dice. You can guess the rest, I'm sure. The whole ambience was straight out of Diceman. The only house rules were that you had to do exactly what the dice commanded. Anyone caught disobeying was thrown out. For those without the mental creativity to load their own numbers with stimulating options there were suggestion cards provided. All kinds of exotic characters roamed the premises. And they would do all kinds of exotic things. It was the ultimate corporate night-out thrill. Magic, miracles and wonder. For a little extra (around £500) you could have the whole experience recorded on take-home VHS. The profits were rolling in. Chance O'Sullivan was on the rise again.

*   *   *   *   *

On Millennium night Chance threw out the challenge on national TV. It had been a wonderful year for him. In January he had launched his Chance Encounter range of perfume. With the public face he chose, there was no way it would fail. He was living in London now where he had headquartered a national string of upmarket casinos. The Main Chance. They were turning millions. Now he was ready for the advent of his new reality TV show *Your Big Chance*. It kicked off on Millennium night.

Hundreds of punters had tried to get on the show. Chance, myself and two assistants had screened them all. And now it was down to a TV vote. As with all of Chance's ventures the rules were simple. But effective.

'So Belinda,' he intoned before the watching nation, 'do you promise to do everything the dice tells you to for one year? To work where it wants you to work, love who it tells you to love, and to go, be and do only what it tells you?'

'I do.' she replied, eyes all lit up like lights on a Christmas tree.

'People, she needs your votes. Remember, only six people can play. Will Belinda be one of them?' Belinda wasn't.

By the end of the voting he had his six.

Sponsored by The Main Chance they would live out one year in a strictly monitored world where every decision was taken by the dice. No expense spared. Though they all had to sign disclaimers indemnifying the Sporting Chance Holding Company and all of its subsidiaries from any and all liability for any eventuality that lady luck might bring their way.

Chance had syndicated the show world-wide. It was twenty-four-hour live on-line and on his Chance for Excitement pay-per-view Cable TV station, and for a small fee (£20) viewers could make suggestions that would load some numbers for their favourite character. Become vicarious Dicemen. The gain without the pain. The tabloids loved it.

At the end of the year Chance himself would name the winner based on which of them, in the view of the great man, had been the most lucky – or maybe he'd just throw a dice – there were all sorts of rumours that this might be the twist. The winner was then going to designate random numbers to six mystery prizes, three of which were worth one million pounds sterling and three worth more or less nothing. Then let the dice make the call.

As the clock over the Thames struck twelve, Chance handed out the dice. 'Throw,' he commanded. The game was on.

It was the TV blockbuster of the year. As with everything else in the O'Sullivan empire nothing had been left to chance and the whole operation had been meticulously planned right down to the random throws that dictated the evolving pattern of rules controlling the game. These took place on the second Tuesday night of every month. Chance had a whole team of people acting as a think tank. Coming up with six options, each of which offered an opportunity to take the game to a whole new level.

Punters were glued to their seats worldwide. The night that the former lead singer of B-list Indie band Cheyenne Army threw a four and as a result had to come clean to his dying mother that he was booked in for a sex change (brought about by previously throwing a one, as I remember) was the night that easily topped the UK national viewing figures record (22.1 million) set by the BBC for the final ever episode of Only Fools and Horses in December 1996. When she reached out and hugged him there wasn't a dry eye anywhere. The price of advertising reached an all-time high.

You see, he was doing it. Fulfilling his vision. Finding his destiny. Chance O'Sullivan, almost single-handedly, was reaching into the jaded, shopped-out, post-idealistic world that was UK 2000 and offering magic. The dice were the symbols, but the miracles came from the soul of Chance himself.

The result of the game was almost anticlimactic. The luck that had been with Chance during his own time as a Diceman rubbed off. Or maybe as Peter Carrol once wrote in an essay on the Magus, 'If he can convince his acolytes that they are magicians capable of anything, such beliefs will tend to become self fulfilling.' Chance read that kind of stuff. Quoted from it on 'team-bonding days'. We all had to learn it.

Whatever it was, it worked and the game produced six happy endings. The Sporting Chance Holding Company made sure of that. The eventual winner, Gregor McLaughlin from Lanarkshire (a former Scottish International goalkeeper, standing six feet three inches tall, with curly black hair, dazzling teeth and a deep perma-tan – though at least one of these attributes was the direct result of throwing a five in the middle of April – won, on a two, the full ownership of the Glasgow Chance Behaviour franchise. Two years later he sold out for several million pounds. Though not on the throw of a dice.

*   *   *   *   *

It was in late two thousand and three that Chance's luck finally turned. When the magic left him.

I'd cashed in my chips by then. Fifty-one years old with a mild heart murmur I'd taken a buy-out option on my Sporting Chance Holding Company shares and gone back home. Home to the top of the Cavehill Road, which had only changed a little since I was a lad. McCoubery's the chemist had gone, and the sweet shop where I used to buy the penny chews long, long ago, but Jack

Irwin's Da's butcher's was still standing and the houses in Sunningdale Park were still solid and dependable. I bought three houses in the area. Well, there's nothing like investing in the old home streets is there? I moved my widowed sister and her youngest boy into one of them and my elderly Mam into the other. Chance told me I was mad.

'You're worth millions, George!' he bellowed 'Will you not go and buy yourself a proper house!'

I disagreed. It was only three million. And anyway I wanted to be there. You know who you can trust when you're fifty-one. And where you belong.

Anyway, back to Chance.

When they brought him down it came fast. The Financial Services Authority officials rolled up to the head offices of Sporting Chance one morning at 7 a.m. At the same time officials from Scotland Yard and Customs and Excise turned up at every Chance Behaviour outlet and Main Chance casino. The money-laundering activity of one Chance O'Sullivan (or to be more precise Yuri Jacobovitch, his main Russian shareholder) was one of the big stories of two thousand and three. Bigger than the Gulf War, almost.

Chance was devastated. He'd brought Yuri in as he put it, to help him go worldwide. Yuri was a Russian oil billionaire. Owned a premier-league football team and all. Chance had trusted him. It would be great to say that I'd had a nose for Yuri and that's why I got out or that I'd warned Chance but my warnings had gone unheeded. Any of those options would have made me look good. But the truth is I liked him too. And I too had been seduced by his billions and his Siberian accent.

It was all down to dealing then. And they screwed him to the wall. Chance had no desire to go to prison so of course he told them whatever he could about Yuri. Which wasn't as much as you'd think. Due diligence, paradoxically, was never a big word in Chance's vocabulary when it came to friendship. Anyway, his bargaining power was limited, and he had to deal away almost every penny he had to preserve his freedom.

'I was born in a Nissen hut and in my life I've had it all,' he told me last Christmas, 'but I've always been the same me inside. Losing all this stuff won't change me.'

One thing about Chance has always been that he was his own man, and he didn't need the shiny things to feel secure. And when he arrived to spend Christmas with me the bounce was almost back in his step. So he'd brought the wrong man on board. So he'd lost all of his empire. Well the dice might have made him do those things years ago. He was just thankful he'd had the whole cresta run to enjoy.

'George,' he said, 'I'm fifty-two and I have my health and no money. You're fifty-two and you have three million and a dickey heart. Who's the luckier man?'

And he was right. Deep inside I know he was right. He'd been too polite to add that he'd made me my three million. And he point-blank refused to accept the half of it that I offered to give back to him.

I don't know if he was regretting too that he'd treated love and romance in such a cavalier way during his life. I do know, though, that he spent a fair bit of time round at my sister Janice's place. Janice had always had an eye for him back when we were growing up, and she may well have carried the candle all these years. Though not a word was spoken to me about it. Nor has there been a word spoken yet.

New Year's Eve we had a party. There was Janice, Chance, myself and my wife Sandra, my Mam (both Chance's parents are dead and his sister lives in New Zealand), and a few of the neighbours. It was a good party as parties go and I was feeling pretty mellow and delighted to be back home and knew I was much better heart-murmur-wise. I could see though that there was a restlessness in Chance's whole demeanour. You can always tell with Chance when he's thinking. And of course he and Janice were spending a lot of time chatting quietly and looking into each other's eyes.

Sandra and I slept in next morning. It must have been about noon when we stumbled down to the kitchen.

There on the table was a note. George – thanks for everything. Why not conjure your own magic? See you sometime. Chance.

Beside the note sat a set of keys. Janice's house keys. And perched on top was a pair of dice.

Appleboy
Kathleen Murray

He created the first child from apples and the second from peaches. There was a high demand for peach children but it was a seasonal craft and a particularly difficult task bringing peaches to life, so those customers would have to wait.

The watchmaker had travelled for two days to collect his consignment, his child. He too would have liked a peach child but could not afford one. Even gathering and donating the two bags of spiders he now carried over his shoulder had put him, possibly his whole town, at risk. He had written to the man who could transform fruit and in the return letter had received the surprising demand. He could hardly believe his luck that he had been chosen. According to local bylaws, the request to remove the large quantity of spiders should have been taken to the Chamber of Town Decisions for a pronouncement but the watchmaker was afraid the outcome would have gone against him. So he had gathered them secretly in the early mornings and kept them alive in jars. When he had a sufficient quantity, he bagged them up, hoisted them over his shoulder and set off.

As he walked along he pondered on the few facts he had heard about apple children – they would never have the gift of speech, they would bruise easily, they could not bear the touch of frost. The transformations were a recent phenomenon and many questions remained, initially about the man's power to transform and latterly about the children themselves, now scattering to all corners of the country. The watchmaker lived and worked alone and was accustomed to mulling over facts and events inside his own head, having lengthy conversations with himself that often ended inconclusively. However he was clear in his desire to take on the unusual task of minding a fruit child, notwithstanding the paucity of information about their needs, lifespan, and capacity to love.

Initially, once the news of the fruit children transformation was confirmed, a considered evaluation took place. There was a period of time when perceptions were shaken to such a degree that it was not unusual to see a person stopping in the street to reach out, touch a brick that had worn smooth over the years or a pane of glass that seemed alive with a sparkle of light. A pulse, a tremor, a connection with the essence, something communicated from matter to soul. Why the apple, the pear, the peach? People turned the question over and over in their minds. It was reported that in some households the women, on hearing the news, got up from the table, carried jugs and bottles of juice and wine to the sink and poured every last drop down the drain.

In certain localities, after more thought and discussion had taken place, groups of neighbours went together to a nearby stream or river. A rainbow of juices, wine, ciders would cascade into the water and, diluted, make their way towards a lake or the sea. People claimed to have lost the taste for imbibing these liquids, preferring water, teas, grain-based alcohol. In truth, no one dared. Many things changed with the advent of the fruit children and still many things remained the same.

The appleboy that the watchmaker brought home was named Clearheart. Clearly a clever boy, mute and rosy-cheeked, he spent his days in the workshop assisting the watchmaker in various ways. At first an object of curiosity, the local people would turn up on a pretext with some question about a timepiece or a query about time itself directed at the watchmaker, whilst their hungry eyes fixed on the boy at the table chewing absently on a piece of cheese or stoking the fire. After a time they got used to Clearheart and came as much for the warmth of the house, as the opportunity to converse with the watchmaker.

The watchmaker himself had a special gift that set him apart. Although he had served his apprenticeship under the main jeweller in the town, it had quickly become apparent that his talents lay in one direction only. He had some ability with clocks and watches, but more precisely with the recording of human time itself. First, he would meet the owner and their timepiece. Then he would take the clock or watch away to his workshop and adjust it until it was silent. After adjustment, he returned the newly attuned time instrument.

However very few of the repaired clocks and watches went tick-tock. Some went tick-tock-tock; some tickety-tickety-tock-tock; some had a sliding quality – ticksy-ticksy-tock; a number had a deep resonant beat – toock-toock. Capturing the life pulse of the owner and synchronising the rhythm of their timepiece was the watchmaker's gift. One woman who had many children wore a watch that just went tick once a year. The schoolteacher had a clock. That clock, if you listened closely, was a constant tocking that blurred into a hum and formed the aural landscape of the children's education. Two minutes before the church bells marked the hour, the bookkeeper's watch emitted a sighing tack-tack and two minutes after tuck-tuck. No two rhythms were the same and on the death of their owner each timepiece resumed normal service, tick-tock. Once the essential life pulse had been captured by the watchmaker and transferred to the mechanism, it remained constant over their lifetime. It was this constancy amidst change that brought such joy – as the body aged and the blood pulse weakened, the timepiece tempo remained as fifty years before.

The winter dragged on and on, not for the first time, but as month followed another long, hungry month people became uneasy. They looked for reasons and causes.

'The appleboy is holding the winter. The seasons have stopped. Spiders have disappeared. You took them for yourself alone. Our good luck went with those bags of spiders. And your house is so warm, always so warm. You must share your fuel with others of your own kind, not lavish what little we have on the appleboy. Children are starving. It is the fault of these unnatural children across the country.'

The watchmaker thought about the accusations. If one thing changed and another thing changed, maybe they were related. Could he ever turn back to the way life was before? Was his little boy the key to unlocking the seasons? A number of years back a rainmaker had come to the town in the middle of a long drought. He carried a great stick festooned with ribbons, feathers and animal pelts. After dancing and chanting, he sank into a trance-like state and remained that way in the main square for three days. On the third day the rains came. Some believed the rainmaker had drawn the clouds from the blue skies; others felt the long summer had been coming to an end in any case.

He doubted his child was causing the long winter but he also knew, in times like these, how people made sense of the difficulties they faced. Inevitably, blame would attach to someone with a mark of difference. That night, the watchmaker kissed his boy goodnight and as he left the room, he opened the top window. Before he had even closed the door, he could feel the icy breeze at his back. Later people wondered if he had always held something back, if he had loved him like a true son, or had the appleboy's origins allowed the watchmaker to keep the distance needed to commit this act.

The watchmaker brought Clearheart's body to a field outside the town that a trader had bought to bury his son, a peachboy who had died at the start of the winter. Many of the fruit children had died at the beginning of the long winter. The trader was a wealthy man and his was the only peachchild in the immediate townsland. Now he was buried amongst pear and apple children. Due to the trader's immense wealth, he had been able to secure the field. As the initial welcome extended to the fruit children changed to fear, it was decreed that their parents could not bury them in the usual burial grounds, on common land, near towns or on farmland. As a consequence, all the fruit children were laid to rest in the trader's field.

The watchmaker buried the appleboy in the most southerly corner and placed a small marker to the side. Walking through the field, he could see many similar markers, perhaps a hundred, perhaps more, spread widely; Strippy, Irish Molly, Green Chisel, Scarlet Crofton, April Queen, White Moss, Barnhill Pippin, Orleans Reinette. His boy, Clearheart, rested amongst his compatriots – Cavan Wine, Appletown Wonder, Sam Young, Eight Square, Farrell, Keegans Crab, Leitrim Red, April Queen, Summer John, Honeyball.

Some years later, the trader visited the house of the watchmaker. He had never before been to the part of town known as the Lanes and the most noticeable feature was the width of the street. As you travelled outwards from the central square of the town with its wide roads and broad streets, the pavements narrowed until eventually there was no footpath. By the time you reached the Lanes, you could reach out your arm from a window on one side of the street and shake hands with your neighbour opposite.

The two men were familiar to each other from visits to the burial ground but had never spoken before. He made his proposal to the watchmaker and then they left together to visit the graves of their sons. The watchmaker started work the next day. Over each grave had grown a fruit tree. He would stand beside each individual tree, occasionally putting a hand on the bark or tugging at a branch. Then he would kneel down and draw diagrams into his notebook. After several weeks of this, he retired to his workshop and was only seen now and then buying food or collecting some supplies he had ordered at the post office.

The next few weeks were spent back out at the field, drilling, boring, measuring, up ladders and down ladders. He had told the trader to come back in three months and the job would be completed. At the agreed time the trader returned and even before he turned the corner on the road between the town and orchard, the air was filled with the noise. Every tree had a little hole drilled into the bark and into the space the watchmaker had fixed a ticking mechanism, each one attuned to an individual cadence. Every child's life pulse had been recorded. In time, the bark grew up over the timepieces but the sound was never completely extinguished.

Pride of Blanch
Iain Wilkinson

The airport is six miles from the suburb of Blanch as the crows fly, ten by the traffic-choked orbital motorway, nine by the back roads and rat runs known to the taxi drivers and the few who bother to buy maps of a place they've not grown up in. Sarah and her fellow early morning commuters settle into their narrow seats and look out the window as the morning shuttle to London climbs into the light westerly wind and banks gently over the indentikit roofs and roadways. The morning creep to the city crawls below, the cars in the early morning sunshine making a near continuous multi-coloured chain from driveway to roundabout to motorway slip-road and toll booth. Sarah tries to pick out her house but struggles for landmarks in the glare of the sun. She checks her watch, wonders for the umpteenth time why she should already be up for nearly three hours at seven forty-five in the morning. Her return flight won't touch down until eight that evening – long day.

From the ground the commuters look at the sun glinting on metal above and imagine being free of the queue. They stare at the bumper of the car in front and direct jealousy or derision at the badge or the year of registration. They read the dealer's notice on the back window and try to picture the garage. Why is a car from that far from town travelling the commuter route? Who are all these people? Inane twittering fills the airwaves. Some of them glance left at the grassy bank rising several feet beside the road and the small parcels of open ground just visible beyond. Not so much open ground now as the road is mostly lined with housing developments. Every development includes a row of houses parallel to the road, their odd-shaped little gardens acting as a no-man's land, a brick wall acting to screen the houses from the road and eventually to keep the children from their deaths.

In his silver hatchback of nondescript make and model Alan sits and idly presses his foot to the clutch. On his right there is an evil-looking wire fence and a hedge strewn with sickly daffodils, on his left another nondescript car with a nondescript occupant drinking from what looks like a baby's cup. Alan thinks the daffodils look nice but he can't help thinking there are fewer than last year. He looks wistfully at the occasional car travelling in the opposite direction. Over there vehicles accelerate as they leave the city. 'How nice to accelerate out of town and away from the traffic; maybe I should get a job in the industrial estate near Navan,' Alan thinks.

In the empty ground to the left of the road there is little movement to be seen even if the commuters had been paying attention. Not even the most observant among them realise that they are being watched. In the undergrowth and the hedges and the ditches of the suburban jungle live many wild creatures. New York has crocodiles in its sewers. Anchorage has polar bears in its garbage dumps. They say wolves prowl the night streets of Prague. In Blanch a pride of lions subsists on its rough ground and pockets of scrub. Unlikely, you say? Don't be daft, you think? Open your mind and take a proper look. Stop on the overpass at night and watch in the yellow sodium light for the tell-tale shape to slip out of its hide and move to scavenge road kill. Take care to remain downwind of the beast or he may find you and take you for his prey. In Blanch the lion is a scavenger. The urban lion can't afford the luxury of nobility. He is vermin. He eats rubbish and scraps and road kill. In an environment with little prey he must adapt to survive. His coat is scruffy and his mane full of dirt. Do you want to know the smell of an urban lion? Open the lid of a bin soon after it has been emptied and you will know the odour. Would you recognise his coat? Find the remaindered carpet in the bargain shop and seek out the cheapest pile in the colour called camel. Do you want to know what is inside the mind of the urban lion? His mind is a blank, a hazy place devoted to feelings of hunger and cold. But deep in the feline brain there are the memories of his species. He has the instincts and inclinations of his kind but he has been forced by location and circumstance to abdicate his royalty.

Oddly while the lion has no interaction with the people his life is lived to a routine dictated by people almost as if they have planned it. The lion lives, moves and eats by night. By day he remains quietly in his lair in the few trees that remain or the patch of abandoned farmland not yet developed. Blanch is a human environment, albeit one that few humans have chosen freely, and it has a regular pattern of movement. In the mornings the people leave, during the day some deliveries are made and the bin lorry makes its way through. At night the people return, enter their houses and remain behind curtains with televisions drowning out any sounds from outside. At the weekend the lions starve for lack of safe time to move about. At the weekend the people are coming and going at all times. On Saturday night their taxis ferry them to and from the city. On Sunday their own cars ferry them to and from the shopping centre. The lion is bewildered by this; his life now has a weekly structure and a five-day feeding period with enforced interludes. The lion is a suburbanite.

Like the lions, Alan and Sarah do not live normal lives in their natural environment. In fact Blanch is a place unimagined by their middle-class minds before the boom left them floundering in the backwash. Blanch is a place constructed overnight to service panic, sold at a premium by the greedy to the desperate, all blind to the shortcomings of the product. The lions are oblivious to this of course, but they are acutely aware of the nature of their changing environment. They know that there are no domestic animals to challenge them for the edible garbage. No dogs to fight them, no cats to pillage the choice items from the bins at night. In the wild the lionesses hunt and forage for food, raise the young, and pander to the male. The male lords it over his brood. He fights other males for supremacy and then sits in glorious monarchy over his pride. They say he'll even kill his young if it so pleases him.

This is not an option in Blanch. The lionesses in Blanch are carrion, the male is a manic depressive. They fetch the most demeaning of foods and supply him with near-inedible filth. He lies in a torpor broken only by infrequent and poorly timed attempts to mate. The females are so emaciated their ovaries are dry. They have no strength to resist and no desire to propagate, and yet the instinct to survive is strong. This will be the last generation of lions in Blanch, their extinction assured as their land is taken and their food supply dries up. Bizarrely, while they once suffered by being forced to eat things far beneath their dignity, they suffer now from the lack of road kill, for shortage of fast foods discarded from cars. As the traffic has slowed even the laziest birds can escape death under the wheels of trucks. The drivers can finish their meals in leisure and no longer discard food prior to accelerating away. With no pets kept in the housing estates there are no dead cats or dogs to find. In Blanch if you want food you have to shop.

Alan and Sarah live in a semi-detached, three bedroom, three bathroom, front and back gardened, double glazed, burglar alarmed home on a street named for some imaginary trees, constructed allegedly to the highest applicable standards. The nominally tree-lined road joins similar avenues at little roundabouts which serve to help slow the cars and give all the streets equal seniority. There are no straight lines in these streets; every one curves and turns to form crescents and drives. The developer's vision is the very opposite of the cramped, claustrophobic, organic and successful areas of the city. No parks or back alleys out here, no dilapidated shops or hairdressers, no cafés or bus stops. No butchers shops to attract flies and no cobblers to repair shoes which don't need to be polished. To get a key copied in Blanch you've got to drive to the nearby out-of-town shopping centre and make your way through the air-conditioned hall and escalators to the cheapest units on the top floor. If you want a newspaper and a bottle of milk drive to the twenty-four-hour petrol station. Please park only in the designated areas, shop only in the specialist providers, do not ask questions other than at the information desk, change will not be given. Toilets in Blanch are for use by customers only.

Alan and Sarah's house is one of maybe thirty arranged around an uneven open green space, as required by planning law X of the year Y in the subsection Z denoting average quantities of amenity space per acre of development. The developers lobbied against such wanton and unprofitable waste but the planners stood their ground, in the public interest. Now The Green, as Alan and Sarah call it, sits forlornly overgrown dividing the houses from each other and robbing the place of intimacy. Under the thin layer of soil many tons of builder's rubble slowly subside. On top the grass is too long and the ground too uneven for football.

Inside their house is pleasant. Nice kitchen – Shaker style – with a granite-like worktop and integrated appliances. The kitchen is too small to eat in but that's why it has a door to the living room-cum-dining room, quite large enough to be either but unfortunately not both. Upstairs two bathrooms are handy, downstairs a third toilet under the stairs is almost too much. Alan and Sarah are quite delighted with it. Alan often says 'The growth in property prices in the area means we've made a shrewd investment.' Sarah says 'Having two spare bedrooms is really handy,' even if one of them is on the small side and the other feels a mite crowded with a wardrobe and bed. Alan thinks it a bit strange that he rarely goes upstairs other than to sleep. He imagines the bedrooms and bathrooms above as a separate place, one he spends every night in but doesn't need during the day. Sarah thinks that the downstairs loo is very practical and saves them dragging up and down the staircase all evening and weekend. Still it is a bit odd that you could go to bed and not have been up the stairs since you left it that morning.

Sarah's mother judges the neighbours harshly by the quality of their sheds and the length of time it took them to install outside lights. The mark of a bad neighbour is to have bare electrical cables hanging in your porch, she says. It would never happen in the genteel streets where Sarah grew up and her parents still live. Sarah and her mother laugh at the residents of the house to the rear, their curtains in alternate colours and the ridiculous clothes on the line, but then those people bought their houses in phase one, back when prices were much lower. She is sure they couldn't afford to buy in the development at the price she and Alan paid. It comforts her though it makes no sense. Alan's father likes to say 'Well, maybe it's not ideal in some ways but then you have to remember that Alec and Susan have just bought in Navan and that's twenty miles out – just think about their commute, leaving the house at seven in the morning and getting home at eight at night if they're lucky!' Parents take great comfort from auditing their children's blessings and reminding them of just how fortunate they really are.

Alan now knows the man next door and Sarah has spoken several times to his wife. They all confirm that the prices have shot up and the houses are quite nice really. They don't know the tenants in the house on the other side yet but they can hear the louder conversations through the wall. Muffled but still audible. Not so obvious when the telly is switched on. Unfortunately this is not a snag that the builder will address. There are a few that he should tackle of course but then, as Alan says, you'd expect a few things to have been overlooked in an estate that big. Fortunately the builder is still on site what with phase three under construction just round the back of Laurel Drive and nearly all sold off the plans already. Alan has a neat list of remaining problems and has tried to send it to the builder but the fax number doesn't seem to be working. He thinks the foreman might have changed as well because that nice fellow who helped them back before completing the contracts doesn't appear to be around the site any more. Sarah told him to drop into the site office for phase three but Alan isn't all that sure he can talk to the foreman in the correct terms. Maybe the foreman for phase three isn't responsible for problems with phase two. Maybe Alan is just intimidated by manual workers, he just feels too clean when he speaks to them.

Under Sarah's prompting he makes an effort and sets out one bright Saturday morning for the site office of the phase three development. The road to the site is unfinished with piles of builder's flotsam and jetsam lying around and about. Unnaturally high kerbing has to be scaled and manhole covers float above the roadway just asking to be stepped on. The show houses are open but there aren't many cars parked outside. Through the open doors of the three side-by-side properties bored-looking young women can be glimpsed clenching glossy brochures and limited intelligences. Outside, the patches of greener-than-green grass in the middle of so much grey concrete promise a lifestyle which doesn't quite ring true. Advertising hoardings show the artist's impression that originally impressed Alan and Sarah. 'Last few remaining' and 'Show Houses open Sat & Sun 12.00–4.00pm' have been stuck on in large red letters. The house style is different to Alan and Sarah's – smaller with higher density to try to keep prices down. There are some apartments and townhouses packed together and the gardens look small and communal. 'Less house for more money,' mutters Alan. 'Pretty poor really when you think we have a nice garden and a shed and three bedrooms for less than what one of these apartments costs. Lucky we bought when we did.'

He walks on through a gap in a wall and into the rough development ground. Rubbish and dust are strewn all round. To the right is a compound of steel mesh and barbed wire. A line of construction machinery is parked alongside. Beside them several porta-cabins look scruffy and largely unattended. The first is locked and appears to be some form of canteen, the second contains toilets and a persistent odour, the third is an office and it is open. The two men inside say they know nothing about phase two and they can't help him. They offer to look over his list though, and nod and coo in sympathy at the poor finishes it describes. They tell him he has a good case and he should pursue the builders. Alan is confused – these are the builders, surely. They again deny knowledge of phase two though one of them says he has worked on phase one as well. All very confusing and Alan is out of his depth. One of the men compliments him on the neat presentation of the list and he is sure they are laughing at him. He retreats hurt and retraces his steps past all the rubbish, the half-finished footpaths and the trolley dollies until he reaches his home.

Sarah is not so easily stymied. She rants for several minutes at Alan and demands they return to the office and find out just exactly what is bloody well going on. Who do these men think they are? At least they could give them the names of some of the bosses couldn't they? What about the show houses – wasn't there anyone there who'd know? Alan baulks at returning with his girlfriend like some little child. He escalates the argument, sensibly deciding that it would be less harmful to his manhood to stay here and sulk than to be revealed to two manly strangers as a hen-pecked wimp. Sarah grasps the opportunity to confirm what she always says about men and to occupy the high ground. She could use her man's complete lack of backbone in confronting the builders. She stomps around the house looking for her two-tone pink ski jacket and yellow wellies. Then she makes sure to add a pad and pen to her handy breast pocket, just to demonstrate that she is no fool and won't be thwarted for lack of a biro.

On her walk past the show houses she realises that it is later than she thought. The blond hostess-types are locking up and shooing the final browsers out to their cars. Some of the browsers are knowledgably pointing up at the shingles and roof, some are blinking in confusion at the grey walls and piles of jetsam and trying to get their bearings. In the end they all meekly return to their cars and start the first of many journeys through the roundabouts to the motorway to the toll bridge. There is a whiff of buyer's remorse in the air. Not for Sarah though. For the first time since they moved here there is something convenient to the house, she realises. She will be able to walk to and from her destination. She recognises this sense of proximity and ease from her childhood and it comforts her even as the light fades a little and the sky to the west reddens.

The porta-cabins are quiet. The doors are locked and the lights out. The line of construction equipment and storage that worried Alan has exactly the opposite effect on Sarah. Behind the fence are all the items they need; lots of bricks and mortar and plaster. Everything needed to complete their house properly but no one willing to do the work. She clenches a fist in frustration then takes a large rock and throws it at the porta-cabin. It makes a satisfying dull thump. She throws another and then a third. She throws one at the window and it cracks. She throws another and it cracks again. Alan is a wimp, all builders are men, all windows are ultimately breakable. She stops throwing. Just past the cabins the rough ground extends for several hundred yards to a line of scrubby hedge, low trees and what looks like water. A stream maybe or some kind of pond. She's never heard of a pond in the area.

In a hollow in the trees the male lies in his usual position, head on front paws, eyes dead. The noise of glass breaking reaches him but he barely reacts. From his position he can see little. The females are in the longer grass below the ridge which runs from the stream. They too can hear the noise but they show little interest. It is Saturday and they are resigned to sitting quietly until Monday morning.

Sarah sets out purposefully across the field. There are road noises from beyond the hedge and trees, muffled hum from car tyres on tarmac. The grass is long too, not where she is but along the little ridges that run towards the trees. There could be anything in the grass she thinks, but then what would be hanging around this god-forsaken wasteland. A fox maybe, or rats or something. She stops and tucks her pants into the wellingtons to stop the rats running up her legs. As she straightens up the sun comes out in the west and back-lights the trees. It looks more inviting now, well worth a quick look. The stream is a bit of a disappointment, no more than a couple of inches deep and full of stones and scattered litter. Beer cans mostly. A cracked concrete culvert proves that she certainly isn't the first person to visit this place. No real bank on the other side either, just a steep mound and some rough hedges. The traffic noise is pretty loud from the other side so she splashes hard through the stream. She has to kick out to get any water to fly up and the stones scatter all around from her soles. She kicks a can towards the far bank and it rattles off the concrete edge. As she walks part-way up the bank she realises that she is beside the main road. Cars are rolling by just twenty feet away but she has never realised it was so close. All those twists and curves and roundabouts are so confusing. On the other side of the road she can see the roof of the shopping centre – so much for finding wilderness, she thinks, and laughs to herself.

The male snaps from his torpor just long enough to realise that something is close by. He hears the splashing and the rattling of stones and cans. He sees the silhouette of a person standing on the low bank and acts on instinct. His instinct is not to fight for his territory nor to kill for food. His instinct is to mate. Not that this distinction is clear to Sarah who has never for a moment contemplated the possibility that she would be confronted by a suburban lion. Indeed she is so surprised on turning around to see a snarling male that she doesn't think to run to the road but instead runs back to the stream. As she falls to the stream bed under the impact of the male she thinks about what is happening to her and decides that she can't understand it. It is too extraordinary, too new, too inconvenient. This is impossible.

To the male Sarah is a disappointment. She has no smell and is the wrong shape and size. He tries to mount her but can't identify the right position. Frustrated he bites out, tearing her arm but mostly finding just polyester and cotton mix. He steps back from her and reconsiders, then turns and lies down dispirited on the bank of the stream. Sarah is so shocked she barely feels the teeth dig into her arm but now she looks and sees the blood. Scrambling, tumbling she gets to her hands and knees and begins to crawl, then walk away. Looking over her shoulder she realises the lion – a lion for the love of God in Blanch, in her housing estate – isn't following. She begins to run in shuffling steps, her head up looking for the porta-cabins and the refuge of the houses. She barely hears the sounds of paws on grass as the lionesses reach her. The impact of the first knocks her forwards to the ground, and she rolls over to look into the face of the other. She doesn't make a noise because she doesn't know what noise to make. How do you know how to scream if you've really never screamed? Her ski jacket has ridden up and the lioness begins to nuzzle her midriff. Paws scratch at her bare skin. Teeth scrape on her face. The smell of breath and fur is terrible, the ski jacket offers no protection.

The lionesses haven't killed often and Sarah is a difficult thing to bite with layers of polyester and rubber. She will die because the lionesses bite her arms and her legs and her face so much that she bleeds, and maybe she succumbs to shock and maybe her heart stops, but it takes a time. One lioness sits on her and bites and bites and bites. The other gnaws at her leg before dragging her back towards the stream, towards the male. Through it all Sarah imagines the view from above and wonders if anyone would look down on her from a plane climbing overhead. The low sun from the west would dazzle them, she thinks. The motorists on the road close by might spot something and come to help her, but then the first rule of the suburban safari park is to never, ever get out of your car. She screams in anger but the hum of televisions and double glazing blocks out the sound. She moans in pain and frustration and wonders how she could be here in Blanch, so far from home.

Muisiriúin
Nuala Ní Dhomhnaill

Ba mhaith liom bheith im' mhuisiriún,
óm bhaithis síos go dtí bundún
im chlár nimhe, ag fógairt oilc,
ag bagairt báis do shlua an tsuilt.

Do bheinn chomh dúr le taobh an chlaí,
fuarspreósach, modartha, díomhaoin,
púiciúnta, iomlán faoi neamhshuim
ar bhuartha daoine, is ar a maoin.

Bheadh craiceann thais orm, sleamhain, slím
é cruaidh is bog san am chéanna.
D'fhásainn ar bhualtrach bó is ar chrainn
ag sú an mhaitheasa astu go ciúin.

D'fhásfainn san oíche i ngan fhios
don saol maith mór, do lucht an eolais.
Do bheinn níos lú ná tor nó craobh
ach phéacfainn suas thar phaiste sméar.

D'fhásfainn gan mhairg ar ghach a d'éag.
Do shúfainn tríothu go dtín' bpréamh,
go sroisfinn síos go dtí créafóig
is stopfainn ann is thabharfainn póg

don mbás, don bhfuarbholadh ceobhráin,
don mheath, don néal, don bhfeóchadán,
don dtaisríocht fuar is don bhfliuchán
don drúcht millteach, don sú sileáin.

Nár lige Dia go mbainfir greim
as an nathair bhreac, nó an púca peill,
an balbhán béice, an chaidhp bháis.
Níl insint scéil ar an pianphás

a leanann iad, an céasadh ceart.
Níl leigheas le fáilt ná aon teacht as.

Is bheinn go sásta ina measc
ag ídiú saoil, ag scaipeadh báis.

Bheinn obann, gearrshaolach, neamhbhuan
ach tá san fíor don daonnaí, fiú.
Ba chuma liom faoin ghrian ard.
Do chasfainn uaithi le neamhaird

is chloífinn leis an doircheacht,
an amhascarnach, an clapsholas,
an aimsir mharbhánta mheirbh,
an ceo ar chnoic anuas go talamh.

Lá éigin bead im mhuisiriún
ag sá trín gcré is trín gcomhrainn throm.
Is beidh mo lámha bána lách'
i ndán don duine seang is don sách.

An 5ú Feabhra, 2005

Morning Routine
Emily Maher

This is not the first time. It will not be the last.

I am awake but I cannot open my eyes. My mascara has glued my eyelashes together. There is sun coming through the window and above my head I can sense him moving around, the kettle boiling, the water heater chugging to life.

I'm wearing underwear at least, which is not always the case when I wake up with sticky mascara-eyes. If I make it home, which is rare, I can usually scrape a face wipe across my reddened visage. But not this morning. This morning is the usual routine.

I remember the first time it happened. I woke with a start, almost fell out of the bed, a single. How did that work? Woke up and looked around and screamed inside as I realised I didn't recognise the room. Scrambled from the bed and dragged my clothes on. Spied my bag and lifted it mid-dash. Left the front door wide open, I was later told. That was the first. This morning will not be the last.

The key here is to keep your eyes closed as tightly as possible. For as long as possible. That way, as he clatters about, humming 'Here Comes the Sun' or whatever stupid tune has stuck in his head from the night before, he might actually get around to leaving the apartment. How does he manage to hum and whistle as if he went to bed with a hot chocolate at 9.30 p.m.? Is it just me?

So I lie quietly, counting the shooting stars darting in front of my eyes and try not to think about the throbbing, swollen feeling in my ankle. He'll be gone soon enough, surely he mentioned a meeting this morning? Far away, I can hear breakfast radio chatter and the sound of a toaster popping . . . water glugging into mug followed by a plop of milk and over-vigorous stirring of a caffienated beverage. Funny how people's morning routines are so similar.

The door slams shut at last and I roll over onto my side and open one eye tentatively. Nice place, I think and sit up slowly, opening my other eye simultaneously. I get out of bed and pad to the open wardrobe where a large dressing gown, navy, hangs on the door.

The apartment is larger than most, a two-bedroom penthouse. Nice. Tidy and interior-designed. He's a stockbroker. That's why he wears that awful cliché of a pinstripe suit and those shiny brogue shoes. The first night I met him he joked he could use them to see up my skirt if he stood close enough.

It's starting to drip back. Cocktails and canapés.

His suit from yesterday is in a crumpled heap on the floor. There are three others, identical, in the wardrobe and a rainbow of pink shirts with white collars and cuffs.

My mornings are not the same as most people's mornings, my nights diverge from TV dinners and fights about loading the dishwasher. *It's your turn, you oaf.* I don't work days, so there's no probiotic yoghurt drink, no dash for the shower before the hot water runs out. I walk in the opposite direction as the suits and suitettes convey themselves along to their matchbox offices to file reports and attend strategy meetings. Ever moving, ever static. Nights blend into sunrises and I make my way home to sleep off the decadence of the night before. I see the dead eyes of the drones and wonder how I escaped.

I open the fridge. Empty, except for a few bottles of beer and some microwave-ready meals from the gourmet deli. And a bottle of white wine. I fish a bottle opener from the drawer. There are glasses keeping guard on an open shelf so I pluck one from the centre of the row and pour a glass of *Wake Up* wine.

Retrieving my bag from beside the red leather reclining chair, his feature chair, I retrace my steps back towards the bedroom and into the ensuite. The cool water cascades into the clear pedestal sink and I plunge my face into the iciness. Relief. I dry my face on the fluffy white towel, making sure to leave a streak of ebony mascara and some neon eyeshadow on its white cloudy surface.

It's the little victories that keep us going. Mascara on towel, wine left uncorked and going stale on the counter. Marble, expensive, impractical. But they hardly matter as I only see him once every few weeks. That's my deal. Never too regular. The great, the astounding, the fantastic . . . roll up, roll up, watch her go.

Make-up re-applied, I slug the rest of the wine and sit on the side of the bed. I take fresh stockings and things from my bag, deodorant and a hairbrush and complete the overhaul. My coat's on the hall floor so I shake it out and slip it on lightly. Minimal accoutrements underneath. When I get home I'll want to wash my face once more and slither between the sheets till nightfall.

The door shuts behind me. Solid, oak. There is post in the hallway and I finger it gently, stroking the letters that make up his name. You have to be careful never to get sentimental. Never, no matter how deep the longing for a normal life. I descend the stairway and let myself out the main door. At the gate, I realise I'm trapped. I hate these apartment blocks, so many rules and four-digit codes. I tread over to the gardener, smiling.

'Can you let me out? I'm staying with my friend and I've forgotten the code. Thanks.'

He puts his spade down and grunts over to the gate. Punches four times at the keypad. I smile in gratitude and he turns his back and returns to work.

Outside the gate, as I fix the strap of my bag on my shoulder and pull the belt of my coat tight, I flick the corners of the notes in my pocket.

A good night. Not the first, not the last.

Owl
Caroline Lynch

She who hunts for food by the moon
in the meadow, the wood, the silver room.
She who perched at the end of the bed
staring at me when she swivelled her head.
She who has a paleness and grace,
black liquid eyes in a heart-shaped face.
She who has dipped into streams for fish,
is hunter of dreams, of wriggling wish.
She who has talons to rip open quick
but wings that are coloured honey and milk.
She who shadows the shadow that flees,
she who is silence or screech as she flies.

The Herbalist
Caroline Lynch

One night when no virgin could be had
to fling half-terrified over his shoulder
half-loving the buttocky feel of his fur,
he called to my house instead. I climbed
on his back, put my hands on his horns,
their points pushing in and pricking
my thumbs, and revved him up roaring
off down the road. After the speed, so
hair-tangle, mouth-flapping fast, the next
thing I noticed was that the trees, the
flowers, the hedges, all bent back as we
passed. He hooked his arms beneath my
knees when he felt me trying to wriggle
free and sprinted north. The print of his
hooves left a ribbon-long-riddle through
snow. He loved the trot across roofs, the
dance upon graves; a leap across the open
mouthed waves and he swung his pelvis
hard against the east. I was the burden, he
was the beast of fur and skin and goatish
sweat. He somersaulted west. The world
swung like an eyeball in a knocked-out
head. When I fell he used the art of trapeze
to catch me with the greatest of ease, until
my shoulder came free and I screamed.
He punched me in the mouth, he dragged
me south. His fur began to singe. He made
me look at the strange grin move on his
face like a desert snake twists on sand
upon land he had salted and raped. I limped
home in the early morning, my garden
did its best – giving me tansy, marigold
and mist and for the worst hurt it gathered
the most tender pick of dock, saying:
Here, use these, they'll soothe your skin.
Where the devil burns you, rub it in.

Sleeping With Ancestors
Caroline Lynch

Oh me, oh me, oh my, this is the long lie – the lie-in in the bed
on a morning when I should be off out somewhere like a street
or a shop or a doing something place, which of course I never am,
but it's funny how the habits of your father's lifetime don't let you
kick back and relax. There must be a milking parlour in my head,
or gut, or breast, with cows bawling through memory to be milked.
I must get up, go out; the muck, the yard, none of these gone things
will let me rest. The pub, the shop of my mother-girl at me too; the
jangle-bell as someone comes in to be served, I hear it all the time,
and my grandparents' voices, all four; diving back, all eight great,
all sixteen great-great, to thirty-two, to sixty-four, to the hundreds
and hundreds. Close the door. Lie down. Lie down on the bed, the
bed that many and me and we and us and ours and mine have made.

Day Trip
Caroline Lynch

I brought sandwiches and a flask.
You brought the sea and you drank
from a seagull's porcelain breast.

Relieve me of this – this expectation
laid out like tartan rugs, crumple-
kicked and thrown across with sand.

The dead seal melting on the beach
is a woman who once loved you; its
leather stench and shape disturb me.

The grasses growing on the dunes
are all that hold the dunes together;
they are nameless under the sky

and they slice the wind into parts,
teasing the notes of a desolate song
out through the gap, where all joined

secrets are severed.

Cabin Fever
Caroline Lynch

Give me a drop or two of the old stuff, the good stuff, the black stuff.
Isn't my womb working hard, pumping the iron in and out and round
about the baby, floating there inside me in a lacklustre kind of liquid?
If you give me a drop I'll give you a kiss of the creamiest kind, a kiss
that takes ages to settle – makes you fat with longing for a deep suck.
It's just I'm going half-crazy; when the house goes quiet I hear noises
inside me, noises like music rolled with laughter. The more the merrier,
come on, you crammed yourself in there once, now it's packed and I'm
a mad-house; my walls bulge out to here, at degrees beyond the point
of collapse.

Happy Ever After
Yvonne Garrigan

We were on our way to The Good Life. For years we'd told each other, and anyone else who'd listen, that some day we'd make the big move, leave the concrete jungle with its smog and litter and rude people and go to live happily ever after down the country. When we found the farmhouse it had been empty for some time but it ticked nearly all the boxes on our wishlist and Jim assured me that any shortcomings could be handled with a minimum of fuss and expense. The estate agent nearly took our hands off when we put in an offer.

We had been in the house about a month and bit by bit things were starting to take shape. I had taken some photographs when we first moved in so that we'd have a 'Before' and 'After' to show anyone who might be interested in such trivia. Jim was taking a break from annihilating the old scullery at the back of the house in preparation for extending the kitchen and we were having a coffee at the kitchen table.

'This is a good one of Rory,' he said, pushing it across the table so I could see which one he was referring to. He picked up his tobacco pouch and began to roll one of the many cigarettes he smoked in the day. For all his healthy ideas, Jim smoked like a chimney.

'Do you think so?' I asked, genuinely surprised at his choice. 'I'm not terribly fond of it myself. There's something a bit . . . I dunno . . . creepy I guess about the expression on his face. It's not quite . . . ' I trailed off unable to articulate what it was about this apparently normal-looking photo of our three-year-old son. I had been taking photos of the outside of the house when he appeared at the window of his room upstairs. At the time I didn't notice anything but now that we had the photos in front of us there seemed to be something definitely odd about the image. His posture at the window suggested he was trying to catch my attention not because he wanted me to look at him but because there was something else there that he wanted me to see. He had this sort of grimace on his face. I got the impression that he was more than a little scared and I couldn't fathom what would cause this reaction at ten o'clock on a summer morning.

'Ah, he was probably constipated!' Jim remarked. I threw him a glance that would cut a normal person to the bone but Jim had a hide like a rhinocerous and was impervious to all but the most blatant insults.

Putting the coffee cups into the sink I worried at the seed of anxiety the photo had planted in my mind. 'Jim?' I began, not really sure where I was going with this line of thought.

'Unhh?' He replied as he licked the gummed edge of his cigarette paper.

'Sometimes I get a really strange feeling about this house.' I stole a quick glance at his face but he was idly looking at the photos and whistling through his teeth as he fired up his smoke, apparently only half listening.

'Well it isn't one thing,' I carried on regardless, 'It's a few little things that don't quite add up to anything much but I just feel myself . . . I dunno . . . it's kind of like déjà vu but not, if you know what I mean.' I knew I wasn't making any sense. 'There's just a couple of things that strike me as a little bit odd.' Jim's ears almost visibly pricked up at the prospect of Something a Little Bit Odd.

'I'm all ears!' Jim was grinning with anticipation. I seemed to have his full attention now.

'I suppose I first noticed something when we came to view the house. There was something about it that just seemed so familiar. I put it down to some kind of sign that we had found our dream house but there's an edge to this familiarity that gives me the chills at times.' Jim looked slightly crestfallen at such a paltry Something a Little Bit Odd.

'The feeling is strongest in Rory's room,' I forged on. Now that I had started I was determined to make him see that I wasn't just getting cold feet about moving here. 'And that's another thing. You know how Rory's been in to us every night since we moved in? Well I asked him about it the other morning and he says he can hear talking and sometimes crying. But I haven't heard anything.' It went without saying that Jim hadn't heard anything either. He virtually dies when he goes to sleep. Nothing short of a bomb under the bed would rouse him once he's out. Said out loud it did seem a bit loopy to be putting so much store into the nocturnal excuses of a three year old who was probably just trying it on to get into Mummy and Daddy's bed.

'And the doors and windows in this house seem to have a mind of their own,' I continued. I was constantly finding Rory's bedroom window open, the back door unlocked when I came down in the morning.

'Ooh, maybe the house is haunted by the ghosts of all the other first-time buyers who came to look at the place but couldn't afford it and were forced to go and live in three-bed semis on an estate in Blanchardstown!' Jim mocked, highly pleased with his searing wit.

'Yeah, ha, ha!' I felt like slapping him for not taking my concerns seriously. I lapsed into silence as I began to rinse the cups, staring out the window as I mulled over the incidents I had just described to my less-than-sympathetic husband. And then I saw her.

'She's there again!' I said. 'Who?' he asked, absently.

'Nutty Nora from down the road.' I had spotted the old woman from the kitchen window, standing on the road and staring at the house. 'She's been looking askance at me ever since we got here. Actually it's starting to get on my nerves the way she scuttles off every time I walk past. And then I've found her standing on the road staring at the house when she thinks there's no one around.

'Right! I'm going out to see what her gig is!' I headed out the back door with Jim trailing behind, I guessed more out of duty than any real curiosity about our strange neighbour.

'Hello!' I called out as I rounded the corner. The woman visiblly jumped. She mumbled a reply and turned to go.

'No, wait!' I said, closing in on her. 'We haven't been properly introduced. My name is Susan McKenzie and this is Jim, my husband. And you are . . . ?' I thrust my hand out, leaving her no option but to shake it. The woman reluctantly raised her hand to take mine, a look of abject fear on her weathered face. 'Peggy. Peggy Morris,' she offered in a small voice, like she was hoping I couldn't hear her and she could escape unidentified from my scrutiny.

'Oh,' I laughed, 'I thought it was Nora, for some reason.' I caught Jim's eye as he smothered a grin. 'I'm just making some tea. Will you join us? Maybe you could give us a bit of background information on the house. My husband seems to think the place is haunted!' The smile froze on my face as I saw Peggy's horrified reaction to my joke. 'I'm sorry. I didn't mean to alarm you.' She looked like she was going to pass out. 'Here, sit down here for a minute, get your breath back.' There was a bench in the front garden and I helped her over to sit down. Jim went back inside and reappeared with a glass of water, which the old woman took and drank gratefully.

After a couple of minutes, she seemed to make a decision. 'I'll not come in, if ye don't mind, but I'd be obliged if ye'd walk me home. I've something to show ye.'

'Curiouser and curiouser, said Alice,' I thought, but was intrigued to know what this stranger could possibly have to show us so we slowly made our way the short distance to her house. She waved us to take a seat in the kitchen and went upstairs. We could hear a bit of bumping and banging and what sounded like something being dragged across a floor and then Peggy's aging footfall on the stairs as she returned.

'Maybe she's got the previous occupant of our house hidden in a trunk under her bed,' Jim whispered theatrically, which had us both stifling our giggles like naughty schoolkids when Peggy came back into the kitchen. She handed me a framed photograph, old, yellowed but still clear. It showed two girls, their arms around each other's shoulders, smiling for the camera. They couldn't have been more than fifteen or sixteen, their dresses and hairstyles placing the photograph sometime in the late 1930s. In the background I could make out our house as it would have been at the time.

'Who are they?' I asked. Peggy looked at me in an odd way and took the photo from me. She sat down at the table, a small, sad smile on her face as she ran a callused finger over the faces of the girls.

'Do ye not see it?' she asked, passing the photo over to me again. I picked it up and looked again at the two girls. And then it hit me. I felt my breath catch in my throat. How had I missed it when I first looked? The old-fashioned cotton print dresses, the upswept hair had distracted me from actually looking at the faces. The face of the girl on the right was like looking in a mirror. I dropped the photo onto the table. 'I don't understand,' I stammered. 'Who is she?' Peggy hushed me back down into my chair. And she told me about my grandmother.

She told me about two girls, best friends, and how one of the girls had fallen in love with a local lad. She told me of their clandestine meetings, their secret trysts, how the girl's father would have killed her if he had known she was consorting with a boy, ruining her reputation. She told me how their love was consummated in the open fields, under the stars. She told me of the inevitable pregnancy and how the girl tried to hide her burgeoning belly from her family. Of how, also inevitably, she was found out. But her father didn't kill her, after all. Hers was a punishment much worse. She was sent to 'relatives' for the remainder of her pregnancy, and when she gave birth to a baby girl in the sanatorium of the convent in a distant town, she was only allowed a few short days with her lovechild before she was wrenched away from her and given for adoption.

The girl returned to her family but not to her former life. Her father kept her a virtual prisoner in the house, her every move monitored. She never saw or heard from the boy again and eventually was forced to accept that he had not loved her after all. With her baby gone and her love gone, she saw no point in living herself. Her father found her early one morning, hanging from the rafters in her bedroom.

Myself and Jim listened in horrified silence as Peggy related the tragic tale, our earlier humour now leaving a bad taste in our mouths. 'That baby was adopted by a family from Dublin. I was the only one outside of the family who even knew that Susanna was pregnant.' Peggy continued, the sadness etched deep into the contours of her aging face. 'It was such a terrible, terrible waste.'

'What happened to the boy? Where did he go?' I asked quietly.

'Well, he didn't run off and abandon her, even though that's what her father wanted her to think. Of that I am absolutely certain!' Peggy replied vehemently. 'When Susanna's father found out about the baby, he wouldn't let her out of his sight. But her mother confided in mine and I overheard her saying that Susanna was to be sent away to have the baby. I had to let Patrick know what was going on. When I told him what they were planning he was beside himself. He had to get her out of that house so he devised a plan for them to elope. He was going to go to her house the night before she was to go off to the nuns and sneak her out and they were going to run away together: Patrick, Susanna and their unborn child.'

'So what happened? Why didn't he do it?' I asked, but already there was a bell ringing in the back of mind. I could almost guess why he didn't do it.

'I got a bag of my own things together for her,' Peggy continued, 'and I went with him. I was waiting down the road here while he went to get her. He was gone for a very long time . . .' she trailed off. Peggy seemed to go off somewhere in her mind, reliving that night nearly seventy years later. After a few minutes had elapsed, I prompted her to continue.

'Like I say, he was gone a long time, longer than it should have taken him to get Susanna out. I was going to go and see what was keeping him when I heard what I thought was a gunshot. Oh Lord! I was so frightened I just ran all the way home. I don't know, I don't know,' she repeated, shaking her head in a manner that suggested she did know but she didn't or couldn't cope with the knowledge.

'Oh Jesus Christ!' Jim whispered. 'He shot him!'

'Thank you, Mr State-the-Bloody-Obvious!' I hissed. I looked at Peggy, her shoulders dropping under the burden of carrying the terrible secret all these years, her face an agony of regret and loss.

'I never saw Patrick again after that night. He never did come back so, yes, you're right, I think Susanna's father must have shot him. And I did nothing, said nothing. She killed herself because she thought he didn't love her. But I was just so scared. I didn't know what to do.' She looked at me, her face wet with tears.

My mother had been adopted. The evidence of the photograph showed that Susanna's features had skipped a generation. For God's sake, I even had her name. She had reached out over the years and brought me here, or so it would seem. That went some way to explaining my feeling of weird familiarity with the house when I first saw it. And the talking and crying in the night that Rory, God bless him, wasn't making up. And Peggy's shock and horror when she saw someone who looked like her childhood friend walking around in the same house that she had hung herself all those years ago. Susanna's restless spirit was still trying to escape her prison.

*   *   *   *   *

We eventually left Peggy to her memories and went home. I went upstairs and sat on Rory's bed, visualising Susanna's last days cooped up in this room, feeling her despair. Had Patrick really been shot trying to elope with her, or had he just done what everyone assumed and legged it when he got his girl in the family way. Was a spirit strong enough to bring a person to a specific place, to uncover the long past history, or was it just the most bizarre of coincidences? Maybe I wasn't related to Susanna at all. Maybe, possibly, perhaps. That was all I had to go on really, that and the ramblings of an old woman, a total stranger, and my own vivid imagination. I'd more than likely never get the answers to all these questions. I went back downstairs to find Jim. He was hitting the hard stuff and rolling another cigarette.

'Are you OK?' he asked, his face full of concern. 'Do you want one of these?' he raised the glass of amber liquid.

'Yeah, I think so.' I replied scooting in beside him on the bench. 'On both counts.'

'Well, who'd have thunk you'd have so many skeletons in your closet!' he jibed.

'Oh I think all the closets have been cleared out now,' I said quietly. We drank our whiskey and contemplated the different times that had ended in such tragic circumstances.

'Ah well,' Jim concluded, 'it seems that we don't have ghosts after all.' He sounded almost disappointed.

'Oh I think we did. They're just not the ones you had in mind. That poor woman down the road carried a terrible secret all these years, and blamed herself. I think she's been more haunted than this house.'

'Do you think we can stay here now, knowing what we know?' Jim asked.

I stood and crossed to the window. 'Susanna died never knowing the truth. If her spirit was strong enough to bring me here, to find the answers for her, I feel I'd be letting her down if I gave up on her now.'

'So what d'ya reckon?' Jim grinned at me. 'Do you think we can be happy here?'

'Yeah,' I nodded. 'Happy ever after.'

The Wick End of Candles at the Close of a Long Night
Ian Mitchell

They say you never forget your first. Well, Eammon was my first. He broke my duck. Got me off the mark. And here thirty years later, almost to the day, I'm taking time to remember him.

Jim came later and Christine in rapid succession. And after that, well, after that there were more – I think anyone whose early adulthood was spent back then in Belfast would have a significant list – but as I say, it's the first time that leaves the impression. It's the first time that sears your soul.

I noticed his fingers first. He'd had some kind of accident with fire years back, and they were all melted around the tips like the wick end of candles at the close of a long night. It's funny how skin can do that, I always thought, trying to avert my gaze. And of course there was the ubiquitous blue curl of Gitane smoke drifting up from his left hand. Back then there was nothing so cool.

We used to sit up in the second floor snack bar. Queen's University Student Union. Early nineteen-seventies. And somehow in there, if you sat at the best tables, you could feel the gradual deconstruction of who you'd been; experience the blurring of the tight lines that your upbringing had drawn around you. It was a dangerous place. Sitting in the fug of the smoke, only some of it legal, joining in the conversations, wrapping your head around the life experiences of others – it was like every week brought a new mental challenge. A new frontier to cross. An old place to leave behind.

It was a strange place, Belfast, back then. It still is, I guess. A hard place to call home. Home for me has always been someplace where you could grow safely. Where you could try on ideas, experiment with identity and beliefs. Get it wrong nine times out of ten, and it still wouldn't matter because you'd still be loved. Belfast was nothing like that. You have to be right in Belfast. And walk on the right streets.

At one of the tables near ours the 'Christian Fundamentalists' used to sit. Ironic name now, given how the world's gone. There was no smoke curling upwards from their fingers. One of their favourite games was to send a message to the porter's office. Would any member of Gay Liberation come to the nearest black phone? Then, when they heard it come over the tannoy, they'd watch the phone in question like hawks. Noting the identity of anyone brave enough to respond they would target that person for months with bible verses and visions of burning hell. Seriously.

I remember one time the Fundamentalists burned the Rag magazine on the steps of the Student Union. Apparently they didn't get the jokes. Anyway, they sang a few hymns, mumbled some prayers, and lit the match. A historic moment for Ulster, I believe they said. Some of those guys are big wheels in politics now. Trying to doctor the Agreement.

Anyway, back to Eammon and me.

I didn't know back then how differently the city treated its children. I had grown up around the edges of suburbia in a succession of attractive middle-class houses, had attended the schools of privilege and had lived totally untouched by the unfolding tragedy that was nineteen-seventies Belfast. I'd even been born into the ascendant tribe. I did not know that there were children whose play patterns were constructed around the intrusion of plastic bullets fired in indiscriminate rounds through their letter boxes. I did not know that a front door was no protection from the outside world if that world appeared in combat garb carrying a battering ram. I had never visited the darkest corners of fear. I'd never met a Roman Catholic.

Until I sat, a Philosophy student seeking a context for thinking, at a table in the Student Union snack bar. Trying to make sense both of what I was reading, and of the world in which I was reading it. Jean Paul Sartre, welcome to Belfast. Kinda makes me smile now.

And that was where Eammon came in. He was one of six of us who formed a study group. At once the most unlike me and the most accessible. He'd come from a place of which I'd never heard. About three miles from where I'd once lived. Like the inhabitant of a secret room in those rambling old homes so beloved of second-rate children's novelists, where the door's always locked and there's a conspiracy denying the very existence of the dysfunctional brother kept inside, Eammon had grown up in a world whose existence had been denied by the keepers of the gates to my own world. My own Belfast. You'd have had to live there to understand its depths of denial.

He could talk a good game too, could Eammon, though there was no aggression in the passion with which he opened up the life he knew outside the University. He brought me out of my ghetto and into the world in which I now live. Argued with me until I understood truth. Told me how it was in the place where he came from. And when those of a less understanding temperament would question my place at the table and would show deep frustration at the slowness with which I seemed to grasp issues, Eammon would smile that smile of his and wave one melted finger in the air. Give him time, he'd say, give him time. All the while, that Gitane smoke curling up towards the ceiling. And me, working it all out.

And so it was that over months, years maybe, I was able to come to understand that the city we called home was, in fact, a different place for each of its inhabitants. That none of us saw it through the same eyes. Or knew it painted in the same colours. I came to see how one man's villain might be another man's hero. One man's crime be another man's act of glory. That the price of privilege is always paid by the unprivileged. And that there would always be outsiders. I don't think that Eammon ever said any of that straight out to me, he just chipped away at my pre-programmed shell, and smiled when I got the point.

It seems strange now to think of the me before Eammon. The me who was so tribally contained. Whose friends all came from the same mindset. Whose ethics and politics were all bunched on such a small waveband on the spectrum of what could be. Who had never been touched with the beauty of diversity. Never encountered the possibility or passion of another way. Didn't know the music in the songs.

And then in February seventy-five he broke my duck. In February seventy-five I crossed a rubicon.

It was the Belfast Telegraph that broke the news. No friend of mine had ever been on the front page before. And certainly not the main headline. For just a moment I was excited. It's Eammon. What's he doing to warrant this?

He had been walking on the Antrim Road, it said. Near where my grandmother had lived when I was young. Where I'd lived with her for six long years. Just down the road from the house I'd called home. The information, even now, makes stark reading. The only entry he has in the record books reads:

Eammon ———— : Status: Civilian (Civ),
Killed by: non-specific Loyalist group (LOY)
Shot while walking along Antrim Road, near Camberwell Terrace, Belfast.

Of course I immediately wrote him a song; I mean that's what we did back in seventy-five. It wasn't even a good one. It was finger-pointing and crass, and the tune was appalling. The rhymes were weakly contrived. There were too many verses. It wasn't how he would have put it at all.

And then as I say, within six months there was Jim. Gunned down beside his firm's minibus near Bessbrook on his way home from work. And then Christine, shot dead outside her church one sunny Sunday evening (a tit for tat thing apparently). But re-runs never have the impact of your first time, do they? Don't ever leave you just as numb. And anyway, I had no more songs to write. They were all wrung out of me.

It's thirty years this month since Eammon made the front page of the Belfast Telegraph, and here I am, for some reason, thinking about the times back then. Thinking about the route my life took since those long-ago days. Thinking about how all of our times got stranded.

Everybody has their tragic stories, I imagine. Even today there's a note in the paper about somebody's brother. Shot dead in Belfast. Bullets don't have a sell-by date, it seems. I guess everybody knows somebody who meant something to them and touched their soul for a moment. Who blazed across their sky and left a glow for cradling secret, deep in some hidden cavern, before the light flicked out. Everybody has their Eammon.

And all of us, I think, keep some kind of inner space as sacred. No matter what or who it is that we believe in. All of us have a place inside us where we face up to the darkness, when the lights have all gone out. Where we remember and re-state to ourselves who it is we are. Open the jar and let the memories all come tumbling out. Face up to our worst fears. And we're always alone when we go there. Always alone. With the wick end of candles at the end of a long night.

The Mortuary Card
Jack Murray

The two-wheel cart hugged the grooves of the mucky track, laden down with the blackest of turf, tightly packed and creaking from side to side. Cha Carey was proudly perched upon a handsome day's work, feeling the bog in his old bones, as he coaxed Teddy the donkey towards home. Just one day shy of four-score years and nothing would stop Cha's annual pilgrimage to Cullagh bog.

The bog was his utopia; when the sun shone it was the only place on earth. A summer's day with a bottle of tea, a bag of sandwiches and Teddy for company was perfection. He wanted to freeze his pocket watch that day and stay as long as he could, rather than facing for home for his birthday celebrations.

Cha was a champion turf cutter, and in his prime no man could match his industry – a one-man turf-making dynamo. He wasn't much able for hard work now; the process was slower and gentler, but no less satisfying. Tea and sandwiches always tasted better after bursting yourself for hours in the afternoon sun. Saving turf was like the cycle of life to Cha, borrowing from the earth, procuring the remnants of millennial bogs, which would return to the soil as creamy ash.

And he was the grand master of all the procurement techniques. The foot slane, a sharp, narrow spade with a wing on one side; or hand turf made by raising, mixing, kneading the black mud into loaf-like lumps; and his all-time favourite, the broad, flat breast slane, which cuts from black wall in front of you. Left hand at the top, right hand at the back, pulled close to your stomach, tighten your shoulders and sink hard into the soft-bellied bank.

The old skills had vanished, replaced by large commercial cutting machines. But progress has its limits and even though the turf was all machine cut it still had to be turned, stuck and saved; a job for Cha, Teddy and the box cart.

A small two-storey farmhouse, four rolling fields measuring thirty acres exactly, a barn for hay, and a few chicken sheds was all he had in the world. He inherited a thatched cottage from his parents and built the farmhouse himself one summer many years ago, when the hay was saved and the turf was drying.

Cha's mind wandered as Teddy fell homeward in the dusk of evening. He had often wished for a soft city job where he could sit, talk, and write for the day and quit at half five, and maybe even earlier on a Friday. On the eve of his eightieth birthday a life of heavy lifting was thrown his way by fate.

His older brother Ramie was to inherit the family farm, and it was either the bank or Maynooth for Cha. He favoured the bank, but knew it would break his mother's heart. She was hell bent on producing at least one priest, but knew there was a pagan stuck in Ramie. As a compromise Cha decided he could get a free degree out of the priesthood and leave before ordination. There was nothing wrong with a free education and praying had to be an easier route than joining the army. His best-laid plans evaporated when Ramie contracted tuberculosis at twenty years and died. Cha was quickly informed by his father that he would be replacing the pencil with a shovel.

Of all the jobs in the countryside, a day in the bog was like visiting a sanctuary. It was his place to escape away from the nagging world, and most of all his nagging wife Nelly. Her voice was as high pitched as a pack of wild dogs eating a gaggle of ducks, and as incessant as the dawn chorus. She was never easy on the ear; he just didn't notice it as much when they first married.

Cha was a quiet, shy and pensive man. He carried his tall, lean frame with a gentle touch and no matter the occasion, he presented himself with a flat cap, a jumper inside his suit, neat and clean, and smelling of Lifebuoy soap.

In the romance stakes he gave the term late-starter a whole new meaning. When he started stepping out with the local postmistress, Nelly Duniry, five years short of his pension, they were the talk of Ahascragh like John Fitzgerald and Jacqueline Kennedy.

Nelly was thirty years his junior. At first everyone thought she was in the family way, but with the passing of nine months, and more, they accepted that cupid's arrow lands in the strangest of places.

Cha and Nelly married in Knock and when they returned home life remained the same as it always was. He stayed farming his land in Chapplefinnerty and Nelly kept her job as postmistress, sleeping three nights a week with her mother in the village.

She was a wonderful woman to cook and made the finest soda bread and potato cake you would ever taste. Cabbage and boiled bacon were her speciality and she did a mean rack of lamb, or chops in a piece as she liked to call them. Dinner was always at 1 p.m. with a meat tea after the evening Angelus.

For a while, at least, married life was good in Chapplefinnerty. Cha was content to do his jobs during the day and sit by the fire every evening watching the television and chatting to Nelly whenever he had to. She ran a good house, cooking and cleaning, on the nights she wasn't staying over with her mother. But when bad habits form early in relationships, they seldom vanish. In truth Nelly was very odd to begin with and got progressively worse. She was not what you'd call odd in a psychiatric way, but odd in the way any red-blooded woman would be after spending thirty-five years answering directly to a demanding mother.

'Yes mother, no mother, are you all right mother, I'll stay with you tonight mother, Cha won't mind.'

Their first five years of marriage were relatively trouble free, but as soon as Cha hit sixty-five years and Nelly's mother died, she began to lecture him regularly about slowing down and stopping working. It began on a monthly basis, but then gathered pace and increased in ferocity. At first it was a chance mention here and there, some idle chat and suggestions, but it soon graduated to serious demands and diktats.

To counteract his stoic disregard towards her demands, she took to making his tea early and chastising him up the narrow stairs to bed soon afterwards. He was caught off guard at first, but in truth hadn't energy to put up a fight. While this was quite unusual activity by itself, she brought it one step further when she began sneaking up the stairs and locking him into the bedroom for the night. She would often go into town on her bike early in the morning for some shopping or to get her hair done and she wouldn't let him out until 11 or 12 o'clock the following day.

The shame was more than he could bear in his head. What if the villagers discovered what had become of him, surrendered to a jailer of a wife in return for a quiet life? Using the chamber pot got to him more than anything, but he never challenged her on that or any of her strange behaviour, because he knew she would take flight at the mere sniff of a complaint.

Eventually she wore down his stubbornness and for a peaceful life he agreed to give up one farm job a year and pass it on to Nelly's nephew, Eddie, and his wife, Cathy. At first he gave up the cattle, then the sheep, the chicken, and the hay, until all that was left was his annual pilgrimage to Cullagh bog, and he refused to give that up. As long as he could walk and stand he'd be in the bog.

He brought young Eddie to the bog for assistance once or twice, but he just ended up ruining a good day out. Too much soft chat and misplaced enthusiasm, and nothing annoyed Cha more than idle talk. He didn't like Eddie much, even though he had done nearly all of the heavy lifting around the farm for the previous few years. He resented having to give up his life's work and in all their married years the only row he ever had with Nelly was after his first encounter with Eddie.

'That young fellow, your nephew, young Eddie,' he said.

'Did he give you good help around the place today?' she enquired.

'He did, but.'

'But what? Didn't he save you from all those jobs around the place? Aren't you long enough at them? Can't you relax now?'

'I can but it's his manner, I don't like him, he's too hungry for his own good. And he knows little about anything useful. I reckon he's as much brains as a duck and a duck's head isn't too big.'

'That's an outrageous thing to say.'

'It might be, but I know his game, mind an old man for a few years and you'll get a windfall, a farm and a house. Well, he'll get no land out of me.'

Cha's best friend, Timmy Tennyson, spent his last years being helped out by a neighbour's son. Timmy was a bachelor man with a 150-acre sheep farm and there was nothing this young lad wouldn't do for him. He brought dinners to Timmy every day he could, and when he wasn't able he got his mother to drop food in. During the lambing season he stayed up most nights to make sure there were no complications, and he took all of the work pressure off Timmy's shoulders. And when Timmy died he left his farm to the Franciscan Brothers Agricultural College in Mountbellew, because even though the young lad was great help he was only after him for the farm.

Eddie's wife, Cathy, was different, she was a real lady and Cha loved having her around the place. She ran her own beauty salon in Ballinasloe and had a gentle glamour that attracted him, even though he would never let on. She had soft green eyes and strawberry blonde hair, and made Cha feel young and alive. She called him Uncle Cha; he liked that.

While Nelly and Eddie were driving him mad, Cathy always listened to what he had to say. She called at least once every a day with news from town, or maybe a message and when Cha saw her car turning in the gate it would lift his heart.

She gave the nicest presents to him at Christmas time, and always remembered his birthday with a present and a kiss. When everybody else was buying him woolly socks, or ties he'd never get a chance to wear, she always bought the right thing. She would pick him up and drive into Kenny Man in Ballinasloe and buy something he really wanted.

Afterwards they would go to Roger's Café in the middle of the town for tea and cream éclairs. Cha loved cream éclairs. Washing down sticky buns with strong tea, in Cathy's company, was like heaven to him.

Cathy was definitely different to the rest of them. While Nelly was locking him in his room and Eddie was wrecking his head, Cathy was making him smile. She made it more than bearable to have Eddie around, but Cha could never figure out why a glamorous, ambitious young woman would bother with an amadán like Eddie.

As the box cart turned in the farm gate, Nelly's last words that morning were ringing in Cha's ears. 'Don't be late back tonight; remember we're going out for dinner to celebrate your birthday.'

Cha was a quiet sort and never had much time for socialising and knew he'd be much happier sitting by the fire with soda bread and a nice mug of tea.

'But we can't stay in, Cha, I have everybody told to come and it's not every day you get to celebrate your eightieth birthday.' Everybody amounted to Nelly, Eddie and Cathy and their nearest neighbours Herby and Helen Hoctor, who had a large dairy farm a couple of hundred yards up the road from the Careys.

Witnessing the Careys on a night out was the real sign of a special occasion, because they never ate out. The last time they ventured out was when Eddie and Cathy got married. Cha still remembered how beautiful Cathy looked in her wedding dress. Because her own father had passed away, she asked Cha to walk her up the aisle. Nothing had ever made him so happy, and the only disappointment was handing her over to a clown of a nephew at the top of the church.

Nelly booked a table in Twibell's village restaurant in Ahascragh, run by a couple from Galway who had spent time in England running restaurants. It had full silver service, complete with white linen table cloths and candelabra on every table. Once their party was seated the nervousness easily lifted from Cha's shoulders and he began to relax into his night out, chatting to Herby about his day in the bog.

Cha was never a big drinker, he enjoyed the very rare bottle of stout, but when the wine list was produced Cathy insisted they all had to drink expensive champagne to celebrate the occasion. When the bottle of Moët arrived she paid for it with her gold card and almost immediately ordered a second, and when that was gone a third. He loved her extravagance.

Spirits were high and everyone was enjoying the ether and the alcohol. When the cake entered the room to a loud chorus of happy birthday, Cha felt content with his lot for the first time in years. For once he didn't care about nagging Nelly or hungry Eddie, and was happy to enjoy the achievement of four score years in full health with a steak dinner and expensive champagne inside him.

Cha thought Cathy was glowing, the spirit and craic of the gathering – talking, laughing and entertaining everyone in earshot. She produced her camera and insisted on marking the occasion.

'Come on now, Uncle Cha, we have to get some pictures of your big birthday.'

First she took a photograph of Cha and Nelly with the Hoctors, and one of Cathy and Eddie with Cha and Nelly.

Then Cathy turned to Cha, winked and said:

'Sit over there back from the table and I'll take one last snap of you on your own in good light. You're looking mighty handsome this evening.'

He pulled the chair back into the path of a soft light which was fond of his edged old face, and looked around to see the smiling eyes of his nagging wife, her fool of a nephew and his neighbours. He felt happy, happy to be here with his family and his friends, and above all else happy to reach eighty and to be alive.

Before she pushed the button Cathy looked Cha in the eye, and in vino veritas said,

'Smile now, Uncle Cha, we'll use this one for the mortuary card.'

On hearing Cathy's words the company fell silent, and in a matter of moments had all made polite excuses and left the restaurant for home. Cha now knew that Cathy was like all the rest of them, watching the clock and waiting for him to die, while playing hard for the largest crumb.

Something Has Happened
Emily Maher

His hands tremble as he lights the cigarette and lifts it toward his lips. A look of calm descends as he takes the first, precious drag. The faces of the three women beside him register flashes of concern. His daughters. They have his eyes.

He coughs, a rasping hack of phlegm, spit and tar. Shifts in his seat and pulls his dressing gown tighter around a hollow, heaving ribcage. One of his daughters gives him a tissue. He wipes his face roughly and then hands the tissue back to her, soiled and sodden.

This vignette disgusts my ten-year-old eyes. The smoke is hurting my throat but I don't want to draw attention to myself by coughing. I tell my sister to stop fidgeting. She is only six. A baby.

My feet dangle from the plastic chair, encased in their new pink-and-white sandals. Brand new, bought today on the way to the hospital. Before I knew that something had happened.

I know that something has happened because we have been left in this room for an hour now. I checked my watch when we came in. Half an hour ago, a nurse brought us to the shop to pick out sweets. I have only eaten one of my chocolate bars. I'm not sure how much longer we'll be here and I might get hungry later on.

My aunt comes into the room. Outside, in the empty corridor, she tells us that Grandad has died. That we must be brave.

He Does Not Love Me
Emily Maher

The desperate forty-watt glow from the bulb in the hallway seems duller than usual. There is a letter on the hall table with my name on it. I read it slowly. Rub my eyes. I feel the first sob rise from deep within my stomach, battling its way up and out of me. He does not love me.

In the kitchen, I open the freezer and gaze disconsolately at the dinner we would have eaten. The delicious whiting fillets are safe in their batter armour, and the army of frozen garden peas sits smugly encased in brightly coloured packaging. I will not open them tonight and I will not eat them tomorrow. They will go mouldy and green. They will become congealed, form growths. They will decompose.

I open a tin of baked beans and I place two slices of bouncy white bread in the toaster. I watch the beans spin blithely round and round in the microwave. As they begin to bubble and spit I open the door and slowly stir the gloopy contents of the cracked bowl. I spread butter on the toast. The beans cascade across the plate and the butter melts.

I sit at the round kitchen table and stare at the floor. Tomorrow I will leave this place, pull the door shut and lock the Chubb lock. The keys will make a dull sound as they fall through the letterbox and onto the curling linoleum.

He has gone. He has gone and it is over.

Defiant
Emily Maher

If I'd known the meaning of the word 'celebrity' when I was five that's how I would have described my day as a flower girl. Scattering petals on the aisle. Smiling at strangers and squinting in the sun. Eating cake on someone's knee as the adults danced silly dances. Harassed but adored sums it up.

*   *   *   *   *

We've been at this for an hour. Me in my pink-and-white flower girl ensemble, perching on the spiky wicker chair. Teddy normally sits in this chair, but not today. Today is photographs by the window and then something called a wedding. Mummy is taking photograph after photograph. Me by the front door – don't scowl. Me in the chair – sit straighter. Me in the garden – don't dirty your dress.

My hair has been yanked to calm and my face and hands were washed three times this morning. The dress is scratchy underneath and the comb in my hair is pinching. I'm tired already and I want to have a sleep but somehow I know Mummy wouldn't like that idea.

*   *   *   *   *

One hundred freckle-soldiers march across my upturned nose. Long red-gold hair skims my shoulders and lands lightly, just at the small of my back. Behind the camera, my mother's lips are pursed in concentration. My eyes stare straight ahead. Pink lips curled apart like the gradually unfurling petals of the pale roses in my basket. I'm holding it back quite well for a five year old. Just about to cry. But resolute; defiant.

Stories from an Old Man's Eyes
Ian Mitchell

'Tell me a story from your eyes, Grandad.'

The old man smiled softly and peered into the darkness, straining to see every face. Capture every detail.

'It was a long, long time ago, Tim, and I was just a lad like you. The summer was warm and long, and the beach in Portstewart was filled with people having fun. There were kites high in the sky, and ice cream sellers and a sand football game going on down at the water's edge. There weren't the cars you see nowadays, and people were lying everywhere across the clean white sands; children running in and out of the water . . .'

Lost in his memories John McDougal didn't realise that his young grandson's eyes were fast closing as he surrendered to the sleep that had earlier seemed so elusive. Nor, it seemed, had he managed to keep hold of the thread of his own story. But then, it always ended in the same way.

'. . . you know, she was beautiful, Tim, she was beautiful then, and she's beautiful now. Your Grandmother and I . . .'

The door of Tim's room cracked open and the old man's wife looked in.

'Sure hasn't your story put him to sleep. Can't have been much action!'

When all else failed a 'story from Grandad's eyes' always worked for Tim. John had a host of them. He'd lived a long and interesting life.

'Come on now, John, it's time to go.'

And taking his hand she led him gently from the room.

For Old Times' Sake
Ian Mitchell

The white-haired man on the dusty park bench seemed to stare into the distance not noticing the football that had rolled up to his feet. 'Hey mister, kick us our ball back,' yelled one of the swaggering eleven-year-olds across the grass. Van Nistelrooy. It said so on his shirt.

There are always birds singing in the park at lunchtime. The white-haired man remembers that she had known their type and always recognised their singing. Would point out their feathered plumage as if he were a tourist in some strange terrain. Which, of course, with her he always had been.

He hadn't been in the park in years. Had she really been so important to him way back then? They had come here and eaten their hasty lunchtime sandwiches. Discussed art, literature and music in some vain attempt to dignify the clandestine with cultural referencing. Before yielding to the inevitable and devouring each other's mouths and bodies in a turbulence of secret yet explosive passion.

And then that autumn Tuesday she had just not turned up. No explanation, no hasty written note – back then of course there had been no O2 or Vodafone to facilitate the communicating of covert schedulings. He had never heard from her again.

Sighing, he got to his feet. All that was so long ago. This morning he had seen the doctor. And now he knew there were not many lunchtimes left. He had come back to remember. Come back to forget.

Money Can't Buy Me
Yvonne Garrigan

He could hear the sounds of revelry from half a street away. As he approached, the house itself almost seemed to be dancing like that ad for a Dublin radio station where all the cartoon buildings are swaying to the merry, mindless jingle. Pausing before lifting the latch on the gate, he sucked in a deep breath, psyching himself up to approach the door, as if he could inhale strength of will along with the cold night air. He hadn't wanted to come here tonight but his father had insisted. Actually, what he had said was 'I'd like you to be there,' but coming from Big Jim it was more an order than a request. Big Jim liked giving orders, almost as much as he liked flaunting his cash. 'Money is power, bucko!' he was fond of saying, the implication being that he had both and his son had neither.

It wasn't difficult to figure out where Big Jim had attained this attitude. His mother was a staunch, bitter woman who ruled her family with a rod of iron and kept a death grip on the purse-strings. Hardly surprising then when, at the age of sixteen, Big Jim expressed an interest in joining the Army; she was quick to encourage him, as long as it was the British one and he didn't come back till he had made some money. "Ye'll die a pauper if you tie yourself to that farce they call the Irish army. All ye'll get from that shower is blisters and a bad haircut" she had declared bitterly.

Ten years in the British Army provided the perfect finishing school for Big Jim. He returned to Dublin in possession of a sizeable amount of money (origin unknown) and an arrogance that could stun at twenty paces. He met and married Connie Brady, a local girl, and proceeded to impregnate her on a ten-month turnaround for the next six years. Mattie was the youngest and even though Big John seemed determined to mould him in his own image, Mattie's loyalties lay firmly with his mother, while simultaneously endeavouring to aggravate Big John as much as possible in the process. Big Jim had done well for himself since leaving the Army and now ran a successful garage and scrapyard. 'Where's there's muck there's brass!' was another of his favourite sayings, as he tried to instil some enthusiasm into Mattie and his brothers for dismantling old VWs and Fords. When they were in public, Big Jim was fond of waxing lyrical about the satisfaction and pleasure he felt at having his sons working with him in the family business. Mattie found it hard not to punch him in his sizeable belly when he came out with this guff. Failing that, he would have liked to spit in his face, or blacken his eye with the back of his hand maybe, or kick him in the back when he was going upstairs; all punishments meted out to Mattie's mother behind closed doors where there was no admiring circle of hangers-on to witness the abuse. But Mattie and his brothers and sisters witnessed it on a regular basis.

when they were growing up, and were on the receiving end themselves on plenty of occasions.

The violence experienced by Connie was all the more disgraceful considering she was such a tiny woman. Standing barely five foot to Big Jim's six foot four, she was a slight figure, a latter-day David to his Goliath. Years of child-bearing and beatings had left her with a hollowed-out appearance and a silent acceptance of her lot. Added to this was the constant lack of money with which to raise her children. For all his wealth and posturing Big Jim wasn't exactly generous when it came to providing for his family. An indicator then (and now) of whether a child was living below the poverty line was whether or not said child owned a winter coat. Mattie had never had a coat of any description in the first ten years of his life, nor adequate shoes, nor long trousers, nor any of the other items of warm clothing a child might expect when their father was loaded. Mattie was working by the time he was twelve – milk rounds, coal rounds, paper rounds, any round he could get to bring in a few shillings to supplement the meagre sums Big Jim allowed Connie. Big Jim badgered Mattie on a regular basis to give up school and come to work in the yard with him and the older lads. Mattie held out as long as he could, he didn't want to be beholden to this thug who had sired him. Also, he knew the path to freedom lay through education, no matter how Big Jim sneered at the prospect of his youngest son making something of himself that didn't include stripping old engines and being up to his oxters in grease and oil all day.

Mattie was a good student for all his straightened circumstances at home. He had an aptitude for maths and technical drawing and was even quite fluent in Irish, a fact which galled Big Jim no end and gave Mattie a small measure of quiet satisfaction.

Mattie had a fair idea as to why Big Jim was so intent on having him work in the yard. Two of his brothers already worked there, not through any desire to bolster Big Jim's wealth or ego but merely because they had both been expelled from any school they had attended and so career options were limited. Jimmy, the oldest of the boys, had been dispatched to relatives in Birmingham at a young age. Mattie could clearly remember the preceding events. Big Jim would hardly be in the door when he'd be barking orders, which his eldest son took great delight in ignoring, or as was more often the case, making a concerted effort to do the exact opposite. No amount of beatings or time-outs locked in the cupboard under the stairs seemed to affect Jimmy's mission to thwart his father's rule. On the contrary, it seemed to make him more determined to resist his father's heavy-handed cruelty. Big Jim could tolerate the insubordination no longer and announced one evening after another of their blowouts that Jimmy was going to live with Big Jim's sister in England and good riddance. Mattie had lain in bed hearing his mother's desperate pleading in the kitchen below. It tore at Mattie's heart to hear his mother begging for her first-born child to stay with her but Big Jim was not to be swayed. Within a week Jimmy was gone. Mattie could still see his mother in his mind's eye standing at the front gate, silent tears rolling down her face as her boy was driven away. Ten years would pass before she even laid eyes on him again and he would never return to live in that house.

Eddie and Tosh were cut from different cloth. Thick-skinned, thick-headed and thick as thieves, they worked in tandem in stripping anything of value from the old jalopies that arrived into the yard, spiriting the ensuing proceeds out of Big Jim's grasp and into their own oil-stained pockets. Mattie figured his presence was required purely to keep tabs on the Dirty Duo and report back to Big John. It'd be a cold day in hell before Mattie would grass up his brothers, not only because it was against his principles but, more importantly, they would beat him to a bloody pulp if he even thought about betraying their nice little earner. Big Jim understood as much about loyalty as he did about compassion and Mattie was happy enough to relieve him of a week's wages to add to his cut from Eddie and Tosh's nefarious activities.

The Sweeney girls largely ignored their father, an arrangement reciprocated by Big Jim who thought that girls were little more than miniature skivvies anyway. The oldest girl, Mary, packed her spotted hanky and high-tailed it to London as soon as she completed her commercial course in the local Tech, closely followed by her younger sister. Mary and Geraldine only resurfaced in Dublin on very rare occasions although they did write to their mother regularly and sent a few quid when they could. Mattie used to watch Connie reading these letters in the firelight late into the night, the heartache and loss etched on her care-worn face as she was forced to accept that one by one her children were being driven away.

It was around this time that Mattie learned that he had more siblings than he previously thought. He was visiting his Granny Sweeney, a fortnightly ritual he felt sure she disliked as much as he but was too stubborn a woman to admit the fact.

'So Matthew, I suppose you'll be up to the yard soon enough.' Mattie could see where Big Jim had got his didactic way of speaking, any question coming out like a statement of fact.

'No, Gran. I'll stay on in school, get my Leaving, make something of myself.' As soon as the words were out Mattie realised he had made a mistake, shown his hand to the opposition.

'So! Not good enough for you, is it? Getting your hands dirty to make a living!' The edge of disapproval was clear in the old woman's reply.

'Nah, Gran, it's not that. I'm just not very good at that kinda thing.' Mattie tried to smooth her ruffled feathers.

'Well, if you don't want it there's others in line,' she sniped, her lips pursed into what Eddie referred to as her 'cat's arse face'.

'Yeah I know, sure Eddie and Tosh are before me anyway.' He thought he had gotten away with it.

'Not that pair of layabouts!' she snapped. 'The others.'

'What others?' Mattie felt the cold drip of dread enter his heart. What was the old bag on about now? And that was when Mai Sweeney revealed, with malicious pleasure, that there were other heirs to Big Jim's throne. All the years he had been hammering Connie and leaving her short of cash, Big Jim had been seeing another woman, and had fathered four more children with her. Mattie stood rooted to the spot in his grandmother's kitchen, while the hurt and anger built up inside like a volcano about to erupt. His twelve-year-old mind span around like a rat in a cage, trying to think up bad enough names to call his father but coming up short. Finally, punching a hole in the living room door, he stumbled from the house with tears streaming down his face. Apparently, Big Jim had set up home with his paramour in an upcoming part of town and had lived a double life for a number of years. While Connie had struggled to put food on the table and clothe her children, Madge had been treated like a queen, her house furnished to the highest standards, her children kitted out in the best money could buy. The house itself wasn't actually that far from Mattie's but what a difference a postcode makes. His grandmother had taken a cruel enjoyment in informing Mattie exactly where his father had chosen to establish his other life. The mean streak obviously ran in the blood.

Mattie wasn't even aware that he was going there until he found himself standing at the gate, staring at the house with such malevolence he would have willed it to spontaneously combust if he had known such a thing was possible. The front window curtains were drawn back and he could see a bright fire in the grate, comfortable furniture, a sparkling antique mirror over the mantelpiece. He thought of the meagre coals in Connie's fireplace, the cracked linoleum, the sagging armchairs, and felt his stomach turn over.

He stood wondering what to do now that he was here, when a well-dressed woman entered the room and walked over to admire herself in the mirror. Mattie stood transfixed staring at the woman's reflection in the glass – the perfectly made-up face, the coiffed hairdo, the smart dress. She was about his mother's age but Connie looked like she had twenty years on her. The contrast was startling. Mattie's throat constricted at the thoughts of all the abuse and neglect his mother had suffered over the years while this woman strutted about in her plush surroundings, receiving all the love and attention Big Jim had in his duplicitous heart. Just then, he heard a car pull up on the street. He shrank back into the bushes in the front garden as soon as he recognised the thick-set silhouette behind the wheel. 'Hi honey! I'm home!' his father joked as he turned his key in the lock and entered the front door. On hearing this, Mattie finally lost the battle to hang onto his stomach contents and heaved the sweet biscuits and orange squash his granny had given him into the rhododendrons. Wiping his mouth with his sleeve, he half-crawled out the gate and stumbled down the street.

Once Mai Sweeney had imparted her poisonous knowledge to Mattie the cat was well and truly out of the bag but Mattie never let on to Connie what he knew. It would have meant risking her hurting twice over, firstly from Big Jim's betrayal and then from the indignity of having her youngest child confront her about it. As it transpired, Connie had known about Madge almost from the get go but was powerless to do anything about the situation. Big Jim eventually dropped all the pretence and moved in with Madge and his 'chosen' family permanently.

Mattie didn't see much of Big Jim in his early teenage years, which bothered him not at all. He continued with his rounds and his schoolwork and helped his mother make ends meet in any way he could. Mattie would have liked to stay on at school after his Junior Cert. But Big Jim had not changed his tight-fisted attitude towards his first family and refused to pay for the books and other materials necessary for Mattie to study for his Leaving. With no option but to leave school early, Mattie was finally coerced into taking Big Jim up on his offer (for offer read blackmail) and went to work for him in the scrapyard, where he endeavoured to be as big a thorn in his father's flesh as he could manage. And yet he received little or no gratitude from Connie for the extra cash he was now bringing into the house, nor very much affection either. Mattie just assumed that the capacity to love had been knocked out of her and tried not to take it personally.

Big Jim liked to take the lads to the local on a Friday night, where he would stand rounds of drinks for them and a few other moochers who pretended to hang on his every word in exchange for their drink for the night. It was to this audience that Big Jim played. Mattie attended these sessions as it suited him. God knows he had to listen to enough of his father's blather all week in the yard. He didn't feel obliged to suck up to him in his own time as well. His favourite trick was to let Big Jim buy a few pints. When Big Jim got up to go to the jacks, Mattie would offer to go to the bar for him and finagle twenty or thirty quid (which he invariably gave to Connie when he got home). As soon as Big Jim went out the back, Mattie was off out the door and into town to spend his time with people he actually liked. It didn't seem to matter how many times he pulled this stunt, Big Jim went for it every time. Mattie could only assume his desire to seem like the hail fellow well met in public, and his reluctance to admit that he'd been had kept him doling out the greenbacks long after he realised it couldn't buy him his youngest son's respect.

'There y'are, Ma, an extra few bob for ye,' he'd say, sticking the proceeds of his sting behind the clock on the mantelpiece. Connie would cast a sideways look at him, sniff loudly and then more or less ignore him and the money. Although sometimes, when things were particularly tight, she'd swallow her pride and Mattie would spot her putting the cash into her purse when she was going to the shops next day. It didn't seem to matter whether the money he gave her was for his keep, or as a result of one of Big Jim's unwitting donations, Mattie got the cold shoulder from his mother. Occasionally she'd loosen up a bit if he brought home a few large bottles of Guinness or a nagin of something stronger, and would accept a drink from him. But there would be very little chat. The drink only seemed to buy him the opportunity to sit in her company. God knows what was required for her to actually talk to him in a civilised manner.

As the years passed he felt her pushing him further and further away until things got to the stage where he was spending more and more time in town with his friends, only coming home to wash and change after work and later to sleep off the effects of his nightly entertainments. Where was the point in spending time with someone who so obviously did not welcome his company? Sometimes he didn't make it home at all, preferring to sleep on someone's couch or floor or, if he got lucky, a nice comfy bed when a nice comfy girl was willing to share with him.

Now, years later, he stood again outside his father's house, same front window, same rhododendrons. God, he hated those flowers. Every time he smelt them he was twelve years old again, snivelling in a stranger's front garden while he watched that stranger enjoy all the home comforts that should have belonged to his family. He looked in through the front window, again. What was wrong with these people that they didn't draw their curtains? Although that was Big Jim all over – lording it over anyone who cared to look in. 'Look at my house! Look at what I've got! Look at me!!' I am looking at you, you old bastard, Mattie thought, and from where I'm standing you look like a shit of the highest order. Big Jim was propped in front of the fireplace, whiskey in one hand, cigar in the other, bellowing along with Frank Sinatra. Yeah, you did it your way all right and to hell with everyone else!

Mattie closed the front door behind him and stood in the hallway. The paperchains pinned to the ceiling swayed gently in the back-draft from the closing door. He walked into the living room. The woman was hunched over, poking the fire, not in any attempt to encourage its burning power, more just to have something to poke. She turned to look at Mattie.

'I thought you were with him.' Her tired expression belied the bitterness in her voice.

'I was,' he said and sat down in the fireside chair opposite his mother. He cocked his head to one side, watching her as she jabbed at the fire with renewed vigour.

'So what have you come back here for?' she finally asked.

'I came here to spend Christmas Eve at home with my mother. Is that OK?' he replied.

'I suppose so,' she returned grudgingly. 'Well what happened anyway?'

'I'll tell you what Ma, I'll pour us both a drink and you can tell me what happened.'

'What do you mean?' The suspicion back in her voice.

'Well, for years you've been treating me like some kind of criminal. I'd like to know what I'm supposed to have done.'

Connie was silent for quite a while, her mouth set in a thin stubborn line, staring into the fire she was now virtually annihilating with the poker.

'And will you stop taking it out on the poor fire. Those coals haven't done anything on you!' Mattie tried to lighten the mood, ease the tension in the room.

'Oh, you're very smart aren't you?! Just like him! He spat you out! You're bloody one and the same you two!' Connie erupted with more venom than Mattie thought possible from the woman who had carried and reared him.

'I though it'd be different with you, that he wouldn't get you from me. But he did! He flashed his cash and sucked you in! He as good as stole you from me the day you were born!' she snapped. 'Every time I look at you I see his bloody face staring back at me!' She was sobbing now, the dam-burst of tears rolling down her face.

'I thought in spite of that you were still mine. But I was wrong! He turned you and he'll go on turning you until you're just the same as him!'

Mattie had never considered how much he resembled his father. Different clothes, different hair, different attitude had made the face they shared his own.

'But Ma, you can't blame me 'cos I look like the oul fella. I'm not him. I'll never be him.' He put his arms around her thin shoulders and held her to him, her tiny frame wracked with sobs.

'Look, I didn't desert you,' he tried to reassure her. 'I had no choice. I couldn't stay at school, he wouldn't let me. So I had to go to the yard, there was nothing else down for me. But I worked for myself not for him. He only wanted me there to spy on Eddie and Tosh anyway. They've been robbing him blind for years only he can't prove it and it's driving him crazy!' Mattie watched her face, gauging her reaction.

'And did you?' she asked quietly.

'Did I what? Watch them? Too right I did!'

Connie's face drooped with disappointment.

'I watched them but I didn't rat on them. What do you take me for?! If anything, they stepped up the operation when I arrived 'cos they had an extra pair of eyes to look out for them!'

The relief seemed to whoosh all the air out of her and she collapsed against him. And there on the shabby rug, in front of the battered fire, the mother allowed herself to be held by her child, while she exorcised all the put-downs and second best. The hardship and abuse came weeping out of her and disappeared into the fire-lit shadows. When the tears had subsided into dry heaves, Mattie released her.

'Look, Ma I don't belong with those people. I never have done. I've been to that house twice in my life but I've never set foot across the threshold. I can't. That's not my home. Our lives were sacrificed to provide that house for her. I don't want any part of it. This is my home, with you, and if that pisses the oul fella off, then all the better!'

Connie gave a small laugh, and nodded. It would never be mentioned again. Mattie cracked the seal on a bottle of Jameson, poured out two measures and raised his glass.

'To hell with poverty! Throw another chair leg on the fire, Mother!'

Beistí na Glas Gaibhneach
Nuala Ní Dhomhnaill

Máire Ní Choscair is ainm dom agus is múinteoir scoile mé. Táim triocha cúig bliain d'aois agus nílim pósta. Chaitheas seal thar lear i Sasana agus níor thaithn sé liom. Ní lú ná san a thaithn na trí bliana a bhíos ar imirce i mBaile Átha Cliath liom. Sa deireadh d'éirigh liom post a fháil ag múineadh age baile sa Daingean is táim ann ó shoin. Tá tigh beag aeriúíl seascair agam ar bhruach na faille ag féachaint amach ar chuan leathan aoibhinn Fionntrá. Níl rud ar bith is áil liom sa domhain ach ná cuireadh éinne chugham ná uaim. 'Lig dom agus ligfeadsa leat,' – sin é mo ghuí agus m'fhealsúnacht uile saoil. Ach má's ea is achainní é ar Fhear Thuas é atá chomh bodhar le slios, má tá sé ann in aon chor, mar ní stopann daoine ach ag déanamh cur isteach orm.

Níl duine is mó a bhíonn ag gabháilt dom ná mo dheirfiúr féin, Áine. Tá sí seo thuas i mBaile Átha Cliath ar an Ollscoil fós cé go bhfuil sí glan thar triocha bliain d'aois má tá sí lá. Ó tá, agus go bog binn agus bliain agus triocha mar ceithre bliana go díreach atá agamsa uirthi, ceithre bliana agus trí lá. An t-am chéanna de bhliain a rugadh an bheirt againn, i dtús mí na Feabhra. Fágann san gur i mí na Bealtaine a bhí an t–action ar fad ag ár n-athair ar ár máthair. Mí Bealtaine na bprátaí nua is na maircréal reatha. Abraimse coirche cruaidh leat! – sin é a chuir an teaspach go léir ionntu, ní foláir. Mar cad eile ach teaspach a déarfá le bheith ag tabhairt beirt leanaí ar an saol is sibh araon ag druidim leis an dá scór is gan agaibh sa tsaol ach botháinín scóir go raibh sé de bhréaguaisleacht ag an gComhairle Condae 'cottage' a thabhairt air. Is dá olcas san mar bheart ann féin bheith ag tabhairt beirt gearrachailí ar an saol, dream gur costaisí go mór iad ná buachaillí, is gur lú go mór an bailiú atá uathu. Ach bhí láimh Dé san obair, is dócha. Is b'fhéidir nach raibh puinn rogha acu sna nithe seo. Rudaí is sea iad nach bhfuil a fhios agam-sa faic mar gheall orthu is b'fhéidir nach fearrde mé an fios san a bheith. Níl le rá ach míle buíochas le Dia Mor na Glóire go raibh Coláiste Íde ann, is meabhar cinn maith ag an mbeirt againn, pé dúchas ónar thugamair é. Fuaireamair beirt scoláireachtaí go dtí an Ollscoil is níor fhéachamair siar ó shoin. Mar a dúirt seanbhean anseo timpeall fadó lena mac a bhí ag dul le sagartóireacht – 'Lean leis an léan, a Pheaidí, is ní bheidh cac ar do bhróga.'

Dá mba ag brath ar an dream age baile a bheimíst ní ró-mhaith an crot a bheadh inniu orainn. Ar an gcéad dul síos is fadó a bheimíst bailithe linn go Sasana. Ba dhóigh leat gur cheart go mbeadh 'Reared for export' stampáilte i ndúch gorm ar ár gclár éadain is sinn ag teacht anuas den dtraen i Euston, nó mar a bhíodh ar na sean-chrocadóirí éadaigh 'Éire tír a dhéanta'. Sinn ag teacht amach as an dtraen lenár gcásanna éadtroma 'cardboard' mar a bhí an t-am san ann, is gan puinn ionnta ach ár ngúnaí oíche, ár bpaidrín ó Chnoc Mhuire is ár leabhar novenas. Ansan ní fada go mbeadh post éigin fachta againn dúinn féin i gcaifé beag i bPaddington nó in ospidéal i mBethnal Green is ansan a bheimíst fanta riamh ó shoin. Ach pé acu caifé nó ospidéal is í an obair chéanna a béadh romhainn, sclábhaíocht ó dhubh na maidne, ag ní úrlár a bhí salach le cac is le cur amach daoine eile. Béarla ar fad a bheadh á labhairt againn, ar ndóigh, ach más ea, Béarla ná beadh anseo ná ansiúd – 'l'eanna leathanna Chiarraí is an 'F' in ionad an 'W' – De Fwight ceawf by de fwawl – agus é seo go léir meascaith le nósanna teangan na gCockneys. Bheadh 'luverly idear' againn is na haon 'Duckie' is 'Dearie' is 'taw' is 'tea-taw'. Ó, do chonac mo dhóthain dó. Buíochas le Dia go raibh Coláiste Íde ann, sin é an méid adeirim.

Ach mar adúrt ó chiannaibhín, níl éinne is mó a chuireann isteach orm ná mo dheirfiúr Áine. Dhein sí céim sa sícéolaíocht agus ansan M.A. ann agus anois cad deirir ná gur thug sí suas é is gur chas sí timpeall is thosnaigh ag déanamh leighis. Is dócha go bhfuil moladh ag dul di toisc gurb í féin a dhein gach pinginn des na táillí is dá costaisí beatha. Teastaíonn uaithi bheith ina sícíatraí teoiriciúil, pé diabhal ainmhí é sin. Ba mhaith an sás chuighe sin í déarfainn mar tá teoiricí aici ar ghach uile ní faoin spéir. Níor mhaith liom a lua cad iad na teoiricí atá aici mar gheall ormsa. Ach rud siumiúil b'fhéidir, níl sí sin pósta ach oiread liom féin.

Ach ní stopann sí de shíor is choíche ach a bheith ag déanamh cur isteach orm. Tóg Dé hAoine seo 'michearn, mar shampla. Bhíos suite ar mo chúilín tseamhrach cois na fuinneoige ag féachaint amach ar chuan leathan álainn Fionntrá. Bhí úrscéal im' láimh agam ach ní air a bhí m'aire ach ar ghainéad a bhí ag peileáil amuigh sa chuan. Gach uair a thomadh sé ina sciúrd reatha lom díreach chífeá an sconnadh beag uisce ag éirí mar ar bhuail sé í is bheadh do chroí id' bhéal go dtí dhá seicind nó trí na dhiaidh sin nuair a phreabadh sé ar barra arís. Ní raibh sé riamh ós cionn an uisce ach cúpla feá cé gur minic a chonac an t-éan chéanna agus é ag éirí trí huaire níos airde. Dá airde a éiríonn sé is ea is doimhne a thomann sé, deir siad. Deir siad chomh maith gur dath na cloiche atá ar a shúil is nach féidir leis éirí ón dtalamh ach san áit ina mbeidh mian aol-cloiche nó cloch mar é go bhfuil an dath chéanna ann is atá ina shúil féin. Ach caint gan éifeacht is ea an méid sin mar anois díreach ós comhair mo dhá shúl tá sé sé ag éirí go bog binn as an uisce gan aon chabhair ó aon aolchloch. 'Cás dó, mhuis, is an neart a bhíonn ins na sciatháin aige, ní choimeadfadh aon ní ar an dtalamh é.

Bhíos ag féachaint amach air seo faoi shéan is faoi shuaimhneas nuair cad a chífinn ag casadh isteach an geata chugham ach cairt, Toyota dearg, is ceathrar duine ann nach raibh ar m'aithne. 'Ó i gcúntais Dé na bhFlaitheas, cé hiad na diabhail seo chugham in aon chor,' arsa mise liom féin, ag caitheamh uaim mo leabhar is ag tabhairt foth-shonc anseo is anseo do chuisíní na dtolg, cé nár ghá dhom puinn a dhéanamh le fírinne mar de gnáth ní bhíonn bun cleite amach ná bun cleite isteach ar mo thigh. Ach fós ní thabharfainn le rá d'éinne nach rabhas thar a bheith tíosiúil slachtmhar is n'fheadarais pé scéal é cérbh iad na diabhail seo chugham. Ceathrar acu a bhí ann, mar dhiabhail, agus thugas faoi ndeara go maith iad agus iad ag siúl aníos an pábhaile. Chun tosaigh orthu bhí fear gruaigeach spéaclach, laistiar dó san arís bhí fámaire fada fionn. Bhí cuma pat-fhiáin ar an mbeirt acu is ba dhóigh leat óna mbalcaisí gur anuas ós na sléibhte arda a bhíodar tagtha ar chuaird chughainn. Fir cnoc go deimhin. Ní raibh dealramh chomh holc san ar an mbeirt eile – balcaire beag reamhar de bhuachaill óg is cailín ag siúl taobh leis agus a laghad san d'fhaid eatorthu go dtuigfeá iad a bheith an-mhór lena chéile. Ní rabhadar ag breith ar láimh ar a chéile ná faic, agus cé ná fuil aon eolas pearsanta agamsa ar na cúrsaí sin, fós ní leanbh ó aréir mé agus is maith atá's agam an rud atá's agam. Thugas faoi ndeara go maith an ceathrar, ach fós líon tocht eigin neirbhíse isteach orm nuair a chonac chugham iad. Níorbh fhearra liom ná rud ar bith faoin spéir ach a ndroim a fheiscint ag imeacht uaim in ionad a n-aighthe a bheith dírithe im' threo. Bhí sé leath ar m'intinn an rud adúirt Bean an Doichill fadó ará leo –

'Fan má tá deithnead ort, is ar ndóigh tá. Suigh suas chun na tine, ith is ól do shá. Ach dá mbeinnse id thigh-se faoi mar taoi-se im' thigh-se d'imeoinn abhaile, ach mar sin féin fan go lá.'

Bhuail an cnag ar an doras. Chuas á fhreagairt.

'An tú Máire?' arsa an ceathrar acu as béalaibh a chéile.

'Is mé,' arsa mise, doicheallach go maith.

'Mise Martin,' arsa fear na spéaclaí.

'Mise Adrian,' arsan fámaire fionn.

'Mise Niall,' arsa an balcaire de bhuachaill óg.

'Agus mise Eibhlín,' arsan gcailín. Bhí blas tuaisceartach ar an slí a dúirt sí a hainm, ag fuaimniú an 'bh' ina lár. Ó Thir Conaill di ní foláir.

'Bhuel,' arsa mise. Ní rabhadar chun hum ná ham a bhaint asam.

'Cáirde le Áine, do dheirfiúr, is ea sinn. Táimse agus Martin anseo in aon rang lei sa choláiste,' arsa Niall. 'Bhíomar ag tabhairt cuaird ar an dúthaigh agus thug sí an seoladh dúinn is dúirt linn gur ceart dul ar do thuairisc.'

D'athraigh sé sin cúrsaí is chuir sé craiceann nua ar na haon ní. D'fháiltíos rompu is chuireas tae is brioscaí ós a gcomhair is bhíomar síoch grách lena chéile. Fuaireas amach gan ro-mhoill go raibh Niall agus Eibhlín geallta le chéile is gur Sasanaigh ab ea Martin agus Adrian, fir na gcnoc, is go rabhadar díreach taréis trí lá a chaitheamh ag siúl síos cnámhdroma na leithinse ó ThráLí i leith. Féach go rabhas ceart ó thús mar gheall orthu. Ní haon dóithín an seanchlaoigeann mar sin féin.

Bhíomar go léir anois ag féachaint amach an fhuinneog ar chuan Fionntrá.

'Tá radharc breá agat,' arsa duine acu, ní cuimhin liom anois cioca a labhair.

'Tá, is dócha. Radharc is ea í seo ná gheofá i gcathair go deo deo.'

'Agus cé'n bá é seo in aon chor,' arsa aineolaí éigin ina measc, fear nár aithin cuan thar bhá.

Anois táim ana-mhórálach ar m'áit dúchais, is aon uair a thosnaím ag caint fúithi ní féidir aon stop in aonchor a chur liom.

'Seo ó bhúr gcomhair amach Cuan Fionntrá, áit a d'tháinig Dáire Donn, mac Rí an Domhain Toir isteach lena loingeas fadó is gur tháinig Fionn Mac Cumhail is na Fianna faoina dhéin is gur throideadar cath mór miotaseólaíochta ar an dtráigh seo a mhair ar feadh lae agus bliana.

Bhíodar go léir ag féachaint go cúramach orm faoin am seo. Bhí a suim múscailte agam.

'Is an gcíonn sibh an caisleán sin ansan thall. Sin Rath Fhionáin, nó Rath Chonáin mar a thugann cuid des na daoine air, toisc gurb ann a bhí Conán Mór Mallachtach Mac Mórna ina chodladh nuair an sheol an loingeas isteach sa chuan, d'réir an tseanchais. Agus an cnoc ansan thall istigh sa chúinne, sin é Cruach Mhárthain, áit a raibh ConCrithir mhic Briain mhic Feabhal ina fharaire de réir ceann eile desna seanscéalta. Bhí sé ina ainm bheith ina fharaire ar an gcósta dos na Fianna ach thit a chodladh air is tá rian a leaba ar an gcnoc ó shoin. Níor thuig sé faic go dtí gur ardaigh sé a cheann ar maidin is go raibh an cuan go léir dubh le seolta.'

Chuireas gothaí na scéalaíochta orm féin.

'Ba lán crioslach agus imeall an chuain de'n loingeas agus iad chomh tiubh ar a chéile go bhféadfadh na fir ins an loing ba shia amach siúl ó long go long isteach agus teacht de chosa trioma ar an dtráigh.'

Bhí oiread fothchupáin ar na súile anois acu. N'fheadar siad ná gur as póirsí dorcha m'intinne a bhíos ag tabhairt an méid sin liom. N'fheadar siad faic mar gheall ar conas a buaileadh leabhartha an tSeabhaic 'Triúcha Céad Chorca Dhuibhne' agus 'Cath Fionntrá' isteach inár gcloigne dúra agus sinn sa bhunscoil ionnas go bhfuil stráicí móra díobh fós de ghlanmheabhar agam is go mbeidh go gcuirfear an seacht scaob orm. Cé go gcaithfidh mé a admháil nách mór na sleapanna a fhuaireas-sa riamh dá mbarra toisc go raibh suim agam i gcónaí ins na seanscéalta.

'Níl gort ná faill ná cloch sa dúthaigh timpeall ná fuil a scéal féin ag roinnt leis,' arsa mise go giorraisc is mé ag casadh orthu agus muc ar gach malainn agam. Má tá rud ar bith ar domhain a chuireann straidhn buile orm is ea na daoine óga a bheith ag fás suas is gan á labhairt acu ach 'slang' na teilifíse is iad chomh dall le taobh an fhalla ar shaibhreas a dteangan is a ndúthaigh féin. Bhí roinnt éigin fearaíochta ar gabháil dom chomh maith, admhaim, toisc an beirt Sasanach a bheith i láthair. Ach níor ghá dhom bheith imníoch ina dtaobh.

'Is an bhfuil na scéalta go léir ar eolas agatsa?' arsa Martin agus iontas air.

'Tá,' arsa mise go bródúil, 'mar is leo a fuinneadh agus a fáisceadh mé.

Ní raibh faic á rá ag Adrian, an fear fionn.

'Tóg mar shampla, an sruthaínín sin thall uainn, threasnaímíst é gach lá agus sinn ag siúl ar scoil. Sin é Sruth na Srúile is é go bhfuil sé éadomhain a dhóthain tagann tonn beag breise lei anois is arís a líonfadh do bhróga mura mbeifeá cúramach. Bhí a fhios againn riamh is sinn inár leanaí gur in onóir don mbeirt gaiscíoch Dolar Dorba agus Goll, mar Rí Ulaidh a bhí ag iomrascáil anseo sa tSrúil i rith Cath Fionntrá a thagadh an tonn bhreise seo innti. Comhrac aonair ab ea é is bhí Dolar Dorba taréis mórán Éireann den bhFéinn a mharú. Bhí sé thíos sa tráigh agus na haon bhéic aige ag lorg troda. Bhí Goll, mar Rí Ulaidh chomh hóg san is go raibh na héinne ag magadh faoi. 'Conas d'éalaís ód bhuime, a dhalta,' adúradar, 'Éirigh chúichí arís, a mhic, mar ní raibh duine dar mhairbh fear na búirthí úd thíos nach dtabharfadh tinneas cluaise duitse.'

'Spainfeada díbh,' arsa Goll leothú is thug sé faoi Dolar. Chaitheadar uathu a gcuid claimhte sa deireadh is chuadar isteach sa tSrúil ag coraíocht lena chéile is ag iomrascáil. Bhíodar ag leagadh is ag treascairt a chéile innti is iad beirt ag titim agus ag éirí. Nuair a bhídíst sínte sa tSrúil do stadaidís an t-uisce agus do bhailíodh sé ar an dtaobh thuas díobh ina locháin. Ansan nuair a d'éirídíst go hobann as, d'imíodh an t-uisce go léir ina thulca síos chun na farraige. Tráthnóna thiar do bhí an taoide ag teacht is d'éirigh sí aníos chúchu. Níor stadadar. D'éirigh sí in airde timpeall orthu. Níor stadadar. D'éirigh sí lastuas síobh agus do chlúdaigh sí iad is do mhúch sí iad is do bháigh sí iad ós comhair an dá shlua.'

Bhíos ag siúl síos is suas an tseomra is mé ag féachaint sall na trá i dtreo na Srúile is an méid sin á chur dem chroí agam. Bhí Martin agus an bheirt Éireannach ag féachaint orm le hiontas is le pas beag formaide b'fhéidir. Ní foláir nó bhíodar ag ceapadh gurbh seacht bhfearr an saol a bhí agamsa im'leanbh ná mar a bhí acu féin. Dá dtuigfidíst a leath! Ní raibh aon bheann againn-ne ar an Srúill a bheith ard nó íseal agus sinn ag gabháilt tharais agus sinn inár leanaí. Cosnochta a bhímíst ón gcéad lá de Bhealtaine amach, rud a spáráladh fiacha bróga samhraidh ar an seandhream. Buataisí ruibéir a bhí orainn sa gheimhreadh, na cinn ba shaoire amuigh.

Catshúil dár thugas faoi na fabhraí chonac nach raibh Adrian, an fámaire fionn ag féachaint orm in aon chor. Ina sheasamh le h-ais na fuinneoige a bhí sé, ag stánadh amach as. Dar fia, ach b'ard an fear é. Níl aon teora le scrothaíocht. Chaith sé a cheann a ísliú go maith is é ag teacht isteach an doras an chéaduair, cé nach aon doras seanbhotháin é ach an doras ar thigh nua soilseach aeriúil. Ró-fhada ar fad a bhí sé, cé nár mhinic gur chall domhsa a leithéid a rá, ó táim ard go maith mé féin, os cionn sé troithe. Sé troigh agus leath-órlach, im stocaí mar adéarfá. Ach bhuaidh an fear seo ó thalamh orm. Ní raibh aon oidhre eile air, cheapas, ach slámas geósadáin an seanthomhais –

'Fear fada lom, ag seasamh sa ghleann, gan faic ar a cheann, ach deilgní teann.'

Díreach d'fhonn is bheith béasach, tá's agat, chuireas ceist air i dtaobh an turais siúlóireachta a bhí déanta le trí lá anuas aige féin agus ag Martin. Trí lá anuas cnámhdroma na leithinse ó ThráLí i leith, níor bheag an aistear é, ambaist. Ceann is ea é ar chuimhníos féin go minic a dhéanamh ach nár fhéadas tabhairt faoi riamh ceal compánaigh. Bheadh sé ró–dhainséarach tabhairt faoi im' aonar agus fós níl éinne agam ar m'aithne a dhéanfadh liom é, ná mise leo. D'fhiafraíos dó an bhféacadar Cathair Conraí is cad a mheas sé dó mar áit. Ní eiseann a thug freagra orm ach Martin.

'Chaitheamair an chéad oíche díreach faoina bhun,' ar seisean. 'Bhíomar an-chortha an oíche chéanna mar dob é ár gcéad lá ar an gcnoc é agus is déine go mór de chnoc é Sliabh Mis ná na cnoic atá ar an dtaobh seo.'

D'fhéach sé thar bharraí a spéaclaí orm.

'Níl aon scéal agat mar gheall ar Shliabh Mis, an bhfuil, nó conas a fuair sé an t-ainm?'

Bhíodar agam anois, ag itheadh as mo láimh.

'Bhuel, chun na fírinne a insint, tá. Agus tá baint ag an scéal seo chomh maith le Cath Fionntrá,' arsa mise chomh neafaiseach agus ab fhéidir liom.

Chloisfeá an bior ag teacht ar a gcluasa, geall leis.

'Eachtraigh,' arsa Martin.

Bhaineas casachtach beag asam chun mo scórnach a ghlanadh is mé ag cur guthaí na scéalaíochta orm féin, mar dea.

'Iníon le Dáire Donn, Mac Rí an Domhain Thoir ab ea Mis, agus nuair a chonnaic sí an íde a himríodh ar an loingeas agus a hathair féin á marú, d'ól sí a chuid fola suas ina bosa agus d'imigh sí as a meabhar le teann uafáis agus d'imigh ina geilt go dtí an áit go dtugtar anois air Sliabh Mis. Ins an áit sin d'fhás clúmh ar fuaid a corp chomh fada le meigeal gabhair,' ansan is mé ag ísliú mo ghutha, 'Cás mioteolaíochta ní foláir don galar go dtugann siad "anorexia" air i mBéarla an lae inniu.'

Bhain sin smut de gháire astu, an rud a bhí uaimse go díreach, mar cén fáth go bhfuilimíd ar an saol seo mura mbainimíd ábhairín suilt as uair éigin. Leanas orm leis an scéal. 'D'fhás iongnaí fada ar a cosa agus ar a lámha a bhí chomh géar faoghair le haon crúcaí aon crúcaí aon creiche agus ní raibh ainmhí ná duine go dtagadh sí suas leo ná go stracadh sí as a chéile iad leis na hiongnaí chéanna, go dtí sa deireadh go raibh an dúthaigh máguaird bánaithe aici is gur chuir rí na háite a chláirseoir Dubh Rois chun í a thabhairt anuas chun láimhe ar choinniad í a bheith ina beatha. Gheall sé leath a ríochta don té a fhéadfadh san a dhéanamh ar an bprionsabal is dócha gur fearr leath na ríochta ná bheith gan choróín. Thóg Rubh Rois leis mála óir is mála airgid is a bhrat is a chláirseach is chuaigh sé suas an cnoc fá dhéin Mis, go dtí ceann des na háiteanna a haithíodh sí. Bhí sí sin suite suas ar bhrainnse crainn, mar a bheadh éan creiche agus í ag tógaint ceann do. Bhain Dubh Rois anuas do a bhrat is do leath amach ar an dtalamh é. Thóg an t-ór is an t-airgead is leag ar dhá chuinne an bhrait iad agus ansan luigh sé siar eatorthu istigh ina dea-nocht.

Léim Mis anuas den mbrainnse crainn.

'Nach duine tú?' ar sise sa deireadh.

'Is ea,' ar seisean.

'Céard é seo?' ar sise leis an gcruit.

'Cláirseach,' ar seisean.

'Ho-ho,' arsa í sin, 'is cuimhin liom an chláirseach. Bhíodh ceann acu san ag m'athair.'

Do sheinn sé an chláirseach di is ar an gcaoi chéanna d'aithnigh sí an t-ór agus an t-airgead, ará gur chuimhin léi iad sa bheith agena hathair chomh maith.

Agus catshúil dár thug sí idir an dá ghéag air

'Agus cad iad san anois?' ar sise leis an dá mháilín.

'Ó, eochair eo,' ar seisean, 'nó dhá ubh éan.'

'Nach ait an rud é,' ar sise, 'ach ní cuimhin liom in aon chor iad san a bheith ag m'athair.'

'Agus cad é sin?' ar sise leis an rud eatorthu.

'Crann clis,' ar seiseann.

'Ní cuimhin liom é sin a bheith ag m'athair ach chomh beag. Crann clis,' ar sise ag cuimhneamh is ag smaoineamh. Agus ansan go hobann

'Agus cad é an cleas?'

'Luígh anseo taobh liom agus déanfaidh mé cleas an chrainn seo leat,' ar seisean léi.

Agus má dhein, do luígh agus ní foláir nó thaithn sé léi mar ar sise arís 'Hú-bá-búna. Is maith í an cleas. Dein arís é.'

'Déanfad,' ar seisean léi, 'ach seinnfead an chláirseach duit ar dtúis.'

'Dhera, caith uait an chláirseach ach dein an cleas arís.'

Thugas dóibh mar sin é focal ar fhocal, díreach mar atá sé sa seanscéal.

Phléasc triúr acu amach ag gáirí agus fiú tháinig fáth an gháire ar bheola an ceathrú duine acu. Ní gá dhom ará cioca duine acu é sin. An bheirt Éireannach is mó a bhain sásamh as.

'Ní amhlaidh a deireann tú linn go bhfuil scéal mar sin le fáil as Gaeilge?'

'Am basa go bhfuil. Cad ina thaobh ná béadh. Is cuirfidh mé geall libh gur manach a scrígh é chomh maith. B'fhada ó bheith ag déanamh cinsireachta ar dheascéalta mar mhaithe le "virginibus puerisque" a bhí na sean-phlanndaí Gael. Níor tháinig an nós sin isteach go dtí lár an chéid seo'michearn, nó in áiteanna áirithe timpeall anseo go dtí an ghlúin seo chaite agus é sin faoi thionchar an chléir agus na nósmhaireacht méanaicmí.'

Bhí an fámaire fionn, Adrian, fiú, ag itheadh as mo láimh anois agam. Shuigh sé síos agus an muga tae fós ina láimh.

'Sea, tá fiántas éigin ag roinnt leis an dúthaigh seo, ceart go leor,' ar seisean, 'agus ní haon iontas mar sin é bheith ag baint leis na daoine chomh maith.'

Níor thaithn a chuid cainte ar fad liom toisc nach rabhas ró-shiúrailte do cad a bhí i gceist aige leis an bhfocal 'fiántas'.

'Sea, tá i bhfad níos mó sa dúthaigh seo thar mar a shílfeá ar an gcéad amharc,' arsa Martin ag aontó leis. 'Tóg mar shampla an áit ina shuíomar an campa an tarna oíche.' D'fhéach sé ar Adrian, ag iarraidh cúnaimh uaidh.

'Inis di mar gheall air.'

'Ó, ní fhéadfainn é mar níor chuala-sa faic.'

D'fhéacas ar an mbeirt acu. Bhí rud éigin rúnda ar siúl eatorthu. D'fhanas ar feadh nóiméad ag súil go mbainfeadh duine éigin acu an ceann den scéal, ach nuair a chonnac nach rabhadar ag déanamh aon seáp air –

'Bhuel, cár fhanabhair an tarna oíche?' arsa mise agus an mí-fhoigne ag briseadh amach trí mo chuid dea-bhéasa.

'I gcom álainn go raibh dhá loch beag ann. Shuíomar ár bpuball faoi chab mór cloiche faoi bhun easa.'

'Ó, tás agam, b'shin iad na locha beaga istigh i gCom an Áir. Sin é an áit go raibh an troid mór ann sa tseanshaol go bhfaigheann muintir na háite na spící beaga adhmaid fós sa mhóin ann, rudaí go dtugann siad "arrows" nó saigheadanna orthu.'

D'fhéach mo bheirt ar a chéile. Níor labhradar focal.

'Dúrabhair go rabhabhair lonnaithe cois easa,' arsa mise leo ag iarraidh an scéal a bhogadh beagáinín.

'Sea,' arsa Martin. Ba mhór an cabhair an méid sin, ar ndóigh.

'Bhuel, cuirfidh mé geall libh gurb é sin an t-eas chéanna go raibh Oscar ina codladh laistiar dó fadó. Níl ach aon eas amháin ansan istigh, más buan mo chuimhne, mar bhíos istigh san áit sin aon uair amháin timpeall ar chúig bliana déag ó shoin.'

Bhí cluasa na beirte eile ar bior arís.

'An bhfuil scéal mar gheall ar sin leis agat,' arsa Eibhlín, an cailín ó Thir Conaill.

'Tá, gan amhras nó cad ina thaobh ná beadh. Ná dúrt ó chianaibhín nach bhfuil cloch nó faill nó gort sa dúthaigh seo ná fuil a scéal féin ag baint léi agus ní haon eisceachtaí iad na heasaibh.

'Eachtraigh.' arsan ceathrar acu as béal a chéile an turas.

Ó, ba mhaith an "t-entertainment" a bhí á chur ar siúl agam dóibh, gan aon agó. Thosnaíos ag cúbadh chugham féin, beagáinín.

'Bhuel, ní mór atá agam ach amháin go raibh cath mór graoi ag na Fianna istigh i gCom an Áir. Ní raibh Oscar mac Oisín ach ina leanbh cúpla bliain ag an am agus chuireadar isteach faoi bhun easa é ionas nach ndúiseodh glór an chatha é. Ach pé ar bith scéal é, tharla sé gur dhúisigh Oscar is chuala sé an cath á fhearadh is bhí eagla air muna n-éireodh sé nach mbeadh duine den bhFéinn ina bheathaidh roimis agus léim sé amach as an eas agus theilg sé é féin sa chath is chuir sé an ruaig ar an namhaid ar an bpointe boise. Deir siad go raibh an glór a dhein sé ag rith chun an chatha ar nós torann crúb caoga capall' –

Thugas faoi ndeara féachaint mear idir Martin agus Adrian.

'Nó an amhlaidh a chualaibhairse leis é ag éirí as an eas athuair. Deir na seandaoine go dtárlaíonn sé sin uair sa bhliain ag comóradh oíche an chatha.'

Ar ndóigh is mé féin a chum is a cheap an méid deiridh seo ach ón léim a thug Martin aniar as an suíochán ba dhóigh leat gur ar cnámh na huilinn a bhí sé buailte agam. Níor fhéach Adrian ach oiread ró-mhór istigh leis féin, ó b'annamh an cuma san air, a déarfainn. Bhíos-sa níos mó ná sásta liom féin go raibh sé curtha beagáinín dá stróc agam. Chuireas an suim ann, agus thuigeas go maith canathaobh, ach scéal eile ar fad is ea é sin agus ní bhaineann sé le seo ná súd.

Bhí Martin preabtha chun tosaigh sa chathaoir.

'Bhuel, an gcreidfeá riamh é, ach is é sin díreach a thárla dúinn,' ar seisean. 'Bhíomair istigh sa phuball an tarna oíche is cad deirir ná gur éirigh an glór seo suas de dhroim na talún taobh linn.'

'B'fhéidir gur éan a bhí ann. Ceann cait nó sciathán leathair nó rud éigin mar sin,' arsa mise, agus imirt an chait leis na luchóga ar siúl agam anois.

'Ó, níorbh ea. D'aithneoimíst féin go maith a leithéid. Adrian anseo go bhfuil an-chur amach ar éanlaithe agus ar bhláthanna aige ní fhéadfadh san fiú a dhéanamh amach ó thalamh cad sa domhan a bhí ann.'

Thuigeas go maith an mothú. Uaireanta agus mé ag siúl na gcnoc anseo timpeall, thagadh aiteas éigin orm gur dhóigh liom go raibh scáil mhór éigin am leanúint, pearsa mhór mhillteach éigin gurb as a dheireadh a d'éirigh an ghealach is an ghrian is an ghaoth is na cnoic is fiú cothrom na talún féin. Agus uaireanta bheinn chomh imithe san díom féin go gceapainn gur mise féin an phearsa sin. Aiteas glan, ar ndoigh, is tá a fhios agam go maith é. Sin é an fáth nár labhras a thuilleadh cé gur thuigeas go maith an mothú.

'N'fheadar an bhfuil aon seans ann gur UFO nó rud éigin mar sin a bhí ann, is go raibh taithí ag na daoine ar an dtaobh seo tíre riamh ar a leithéidí, ó bhfianaise ar a bhfuil de scéalta ar dhéithe agus laochra ag baint leis an áit.' B'shin Martin.

'Ó, sórt éigin "Bermuda Triangle" ach é a bheith ar thalamh?' arsa Niall, an balcaire cas, á fhreagairt. 'Ó mhuise, an iomarca de léithéidí Van Danniken atá léite agatsa, a dhuine.'

Ní raibh aon fhreagra agam féin ar an gceist agus bhíos fós im' thost. Ach cinnte ba sheórdán gaoithe é, ceann des na camfheothainní obann láidre a bhuaileann aniar idir na sléibhte arda. Cócaí a thugann siad anseo timpeall orthu. Is dochreidte an cuma ina dtagann siad timpeall ort go hobann i nduibheagán sléibhe, go háirithe aon áit go mbíonn loch ann, ar chuma Com an Áir, is ansan, taréis an dúthaigh a threasnú de thaipeagan, bíonn siad imithe arís, gan cúis, gan áireamh. Ach an té ná beadh sean-thaithí aige ar a leithéidí, ní thuigfeadh sé go deo an diamhaireacht a ghabhann leo is an sceimhle obann a bhuailfeadh istigh id chroí agus istigh lena dteacht is lena n-imeacht. Ionas nárbh aon ionadh leat na seandaoine ag trácht ar phúcaí agus ar laochra, ar dhéithe agus ar shí ghaoithe. Ite ina mbeathaidh ar fad ag an 'nervous' is piseoga a bhí na seandaoine chéanna ach mar sin féin nár dhiabhail an crot a chuireadar an 'nervous' chéanna maidir le laocha, púcaí agus mná sí. Bhí míniú nua ag lucht na seandálaíochta ar na spící adhmaid sin a ghaibhtear istigh i gCom an Áir ach tá an míniú chomh leamh, staidéartha sin go bhfuil sé imithe glan as mo chuimhne. Rud éigin i dtaobh daoine na luath-chréaoise a bheith ag seilg fianna agus eilití leo. Go b'ann a chuiridís ar an dtalamh iad agus tóir á chur ar na fianna acu, is go leonaidíst cuid acu, agus ansan gurbh fhusaide go mór a bheireadh na fiagaithe orthu. Is fada fairsing idir é agus samhlaíocht an phobail lena scéalta ar Oisín is Oscar is na slóite ag troid le chéile istigh sa gleann leis na saigheada chéanna. Ach féach gur mhair an scéal Fiannaíochta anuas trís na mílte bliain go forleithidiúil i mbéal na ndaoine murab ionann is scéal na n-eolaithe nach mbeidh riamh ach ag an mionlach le léan na leabhartha throma orthu . . . Bhíos imithe siar go maith ar bhóithrín na smaointe mar níor bhraitheas faic go dtí go bhfeaca ar éirí as a gcathaoireacha mo cheathrar cuairteóir, is gothaí imeachta á gcur acu orthu féin.

'Ná níl aon deamhadh oraibh, an bhfuil?' arsa mise.

'Chun na fírínne a insint, tá, ar shlí, mar teastaíonn uaim smut don Iarthar, ceann Sléibhe is na hOileáin a theaspáint don mbeirt Shasanach seo,' arsa Niall, agus é ag cur béime ar an bhfocal Sasanach a bhain gáire astu, pé ciall príomháideach a bhí acu lena leithéid. Ní fhacasa go raibh aon chúis gáire ann.

'I dteannta a chéile atánn sibh ag taisteal mar sin' – chuir an deifir idir feisteas sléibhe mo bheirt Sasanach is an chairt breá nua a bhí á thiomáint ag Niall sórt éigin mearthail orm.

'Bhuel, sea is ní hea,' arsa Martin ag soiléiriú na faidhbe, 'mar adúrt shiúl Adrian is mé féin anuas na Leithinse is bhuaileamair leis an mbeirt eile seo aréir de thimpist glan san ionad campála os cionn an ospidéil sa Daingean. Bhíos-sa thíos anso aon uair amháin cheana, led dheirfiúr Áine,'

(Cá rabhas-sa, n'fheadar, an uair sin, i Sasana is dócha.)

'. . . agus ba bhreá liom go bhfeicfeadh Eibhlín an taobh seo tíre,' arsa Martin.

('Áine, dheirfiúirín, tá d'áit seo líonta cheana féin, is é de dhánaíocht ann a bheith ag maoimh le bean eile ar an rud a theaspáinis dó.')

'Tá suim speisialta agamsa sna "clachain",' arsa Adrian. Ar ndoigh is ar Béarla a bhí sé ag caint is an fuaimniú chéanna aige ar an bhfocal deireanach agus a bheadh agat ar an bhfocal 'lachain'. Ainniseoir eile nár chuala trácht riamh ar an síneadh fada!

'Clocháin,' arsa mise, á cheartú. Ró-dhéanach a chuala mé féin agus gur thuigeas canathaobh nach deacair do dhaoine mé a aithin gan dua mar mháistreás scoile.

'Clocháin,' ar seiseann, lagbhríoch go maith.

Go hobann bhuail náire mé as bheith chomh teann san air.

'Bhfuil a fhios agaibh cad a dhéanfad,' arsa mise. 'Raghadsa timpeall in bhúr dteannta is beidh mar threóraí agaibh is teaspáinfidh mé na háiteanna go léir díbh is inseoidh mé na scéalta díbh a ghabhann le gach áit acu,' an méid is cuimhin liom díobh, adúrt im' bholg, mar n'fheadar éinne cén fhaid ó bhí aon ní dá leithéid déanta agam, mo mhallacht cheana féin ar an dtaom aitis a thug orm a leithéid ará in aon chor.

Ach bhí sé ráite is iad tógtha go maith leis mar scéal. B'fhada ó Bhean an Doichill anois mé. Cad eile a bhí le déanamh agam an tráthnóna breá Lughnasa seo. Nár mhór an trua é fanacht istigh ar lá mar é, mar go deimhin peata lae i gceart ab ea é, an spéir go deas gorm is leoithne fionnuair ann nach raibh aon nimh innti. B'fhada ó bhí tráthnóna chomh breá san againn i mbliana agus b'fhéidir for fada arís go mbeadh.

Thugas mo chairt féin liom agus chuireamair chun bóthair. Bhí beirt na gcnoc agamsa agus an bheirt eile ina gcarbad craorag féin. Nuair a ghabhaimir siar thar an séipéal in Ard a' Bhóthair thugas dáta a aththógála dóibh, 1882, is d'insíos conas a bhí sé roimhe sin thall ar imeall an pharóiste, áit a bhfuil an scoil Náisiúnta anois i gCeann Trá, áit go dtáinig an dá shean-pharóiste Cill Dromad agus Fionntrá le cheile. Conas gurb é seo an sean-nós Ceilteach, na cealla nó na hionaid bheannaithe a thógaint ar an dteorainn, seachas i lár na dúthaí istigh mar a dheineadh na Rómhánach. Conas gurb ionad ana thabhachtach é an táirseach i meon na Sean-Ghael, is gurb é sin an chúis gur ceart 'Dé do bheatha isteach' ará le duine ag dul thar táirseach toisc gurb ann is mó a bheadh gá aige do chabhair Dé, i gcoinne ionsaí na ndeamhan is na bpúcaí. Conas gur mó rí is laoch a maraíodh ins na scéalta is iad ag gabháil thar táirsigh is gur chuma an táirseach tí é nó an táirseach idir lá agus oíche nó idir séasúr amháin is séasúr eile ar chuma féile na Samhna a bhí romhainn. Ag gabháil siar thar Chill Mhic a' Domhnaigh dúinn mhíníos dóibh gurb ann a chónaigh muintir Pheig Sayers sar ar aistríodar siar go talamh nach raibh leath chomh maith leis i mBaile Bhiocáire, mar gur cheap an mháthair bhocht gurb iad na púcaí ón lios mór seo ar dheis a bhí ag ardú a cuid leanbh nuabheirthe leothu i slí is gur cailleadh naonúr díobh i ndiaidh a chéile. Gur ón gCuan a tháinig muintir Sayers an chéadlá, ó bhaile an Chuain Uachtaraigh is gur fear ó Chorcaigh darbh ainm dó Leahy a chaith amach as an mbaile sin iad agus a bhánaigh trí baile iomlán gan chreideamh gan choinsias sa bhliain 1867. Níos sia siar an bóthar theaspáineas Cuas Crom dóibh is d'insíos dóibh conas go raibh sé ainmnithe ó Chrom Dubh, an dia págánach. Is conas go bhfuil pátrún in onóir dó fós ar siúl sa Chlochán, i dtaobh thíos de chnoc, ar Dhomhnach Chrom Duibh. D'insíos an scéal dóibh mar gheall ar an t-aighneas a d'éirigh idir é féin agus Naomh Bréanainn, nuair a bhí an naomh ag tógaint séipéile dó féin sa pharóiste. Conas mar a ghearr Crom Dubh fiacha bia agus oibrithe agus ábhar tógála ar an naomh. Conas mar ar éiligh sé meachaint a thairbh féin d'ór. Conas a chuir an naomh an tarbh ar thaobh amháin des na scálaí agus gur scrígh sé an tÁibhé Máire ar phíosa páipéir ar an dtaobh eile den scála is gur throime an tÁibhé Máire ná an tarbh is nuair a chonaic Crom Dubh an méid seo gur dhein Críostaí dó ar an spota. Theaspáineas dóibh Lic Caoil agus Tráigh Caoil ó dheas mar ar tháinig corp Caoil Mhic Criomhthain i dtír taréis dó an t-allúrach deireannach a bharú i gCath Fionntrá, sé sin Fiannachtach Fiaclach a bhí ag éaló leis ina bhád. Shnámh Caol, a bhí i gcrólínntibh an bháis cheana féin, snámhaigh sé amach go dtí an bád chuige is cheap mo dhuine gur ceann dá mhuintir féin a bhí aige is chuir sé a láimh síos chuige is leis sin gur thug Caol aon tarrach maith láidir amach as a chorp is gur thóg sé glan amach as an mbád é is gur thiteadar lena chéile síos go dtí grean agus grinneal na mara. Agus de réir na seandaoine is é a bhí i Lic Caoil ná corp Chaoil Mhic Cruimhtheann is é reóite ina chloch. Nach Lic Caoil a thugann muintir an Daingin air níos mó ach 'Patrick's Point', i ngeall ar tráléar dá gcuid féin a chuaigh síos ann ins na fitheadaí, nuair a thit a chodladh ar an gcriú ar fad is gur chuaigh an bád in airde ar an gcarraigh. Gurb shin agat dinnseanchas na haimsire seo. Slán beo le Cath Fionntrá agus leis an seanaimsir. Gnáth aos óg na linne seo ní bheadh aon tuairim acu ó thalamh cad é ná cá bhfuil Lic Caoil. Ach táimse an-eolasach mar bhean tuaithe. Is mór an seó ar fad an fhoghlaim atá orm. Chuirfinn cosa faoi chearca duit. Dhéanfainn cat is dhá eireaball duit. Tá fios fátha an aon-scéil agam. Bhí tráth dem shaol ann is bhí a fhios agam cé méid míle slí nárbh fholáir do dhuine colúin an Pharthenon i gCathair Athéine na Gréige a árdú cruinn díreach aníos san aer chun go dteangmhóidís lena chéile. (Freagra; a hocht míle.) Féach ar sin mar chuimhne. Ó, ní haon dóichín an sean-chloigeann. Eolas gan éifeacht é go léir nó cén cabhair do dhuine colúin an Pharthenon is é ag tuilleamh a bheatha. Ach b'shin é an córas oideachais a bhí suas le mo linn; eolas, eolas, eolas. Líon suas ár gceannaigh le blodhtracha eolais is le carraigreacha móra Béarla ar eagla go dtaibhseófaí aon smaoineamh dúinn i ngan fhios don eaglais is go mbéarfadh sé leis sin. Eolas, eolas, eolas. Is é a trí déag an préamh ciúbach ar . . . Thit Constantinople faoi ionnraidh na dTurcach sa bhiain 1453. Is iad na mná céile a bhí ag Annraoi a hocht, rí Shasana ná . . . agus Béarla, Béarla, Béarla, carraigreacha móra dó . . . 'There is no erosion without sedimentation' 'In the course of my peregrinations while pursuing my constitutional . . .' Ó mhuise, pé méid maitheasa a dhein sé dúinn, an t-eolas chéanna.

Liom féin a bhíos á rá seo ar ndóigh, go príomháideach, istigh im'bholg. Ós árd, bhíos ag teaspáint mo chuid eolais logánta don mbeirt Shasanach, is mé ar mo theann dílis réillthínní a chur orthu. Admhaím go raibh saghas éigin breac-éilimh agam ar an bhfámaire fionn, Adrian. Bhuel, munar éileamh i gceart é bhí suim éigin agam ann. Duine éigin eile a chuir sé i gcuimhne dhom, fear go raibh aithne agam air fadó riamh nuair a chaitheas an seal sin ag obair i Sasana. Bhí an déanamh chéanna ag roinnt leis, é ard fada fionn. Bhí, agus an meon aigne chomh maith. Agus an neamhspleáchas. Daoine den tsaghas sin, is breá liom iad agus is fuath liom iad ag an am chéanna. Dúshlán dom is ea a gcuid neamhspleáchais. Sin é an fáth go díreach nach mbíonn aon chat agam sa tigh. Is ní maith liom madra a bheith agam sa tigh ach oiread mar bíonn siad salach procach, is bíonn boladh ar na haon áit uaidh agus ruainní fionnaidh ar na cathaoireacha. Pe scéal é níor chleachtamair riamh anseo timpeall madra a bheith sa tigh againn. An iomad de shaol an Ghorta a chuirfeadh sé i gcuimhne dhúinn, is dócha, guairí na muice faoin leaba cnaiste ag scríobadh ár gcosa, an buaile i mbéal an dorais agus i dteannta leis eagla an fhiabhrais. Crústadh maith agus lascadh cic a gheobhadh aon ghadhar go mbeadh sé de dhánaíocht ann a shoc a shá isteach thar dhoras. Ach ní hin é an fáth in aon chor nach maith liom cait. Tá cúis eile ar fad agam orthu. Ní féidir liom mo mhéar a leagadh air go cruinn ach tá baint éigin aige leis an bhfear fad fionn seo, Adrian. Ó tá se dorcha, doimhin, corrach. Tá aithne mhaith agam ar a leithéid.

Bhíomair tagtha faoin am seo go dti Leacacha Fán agus go dtí an Dun Beag, dún binne ón aois iarann. Chuamair síos á fhéachaint. Ceapaimse go bhfuil sé ceart go leor ach bhíodar seo an-thógta ar fad leis. Bhí na faillreacha timpeall air lán de bhláthanna fiáine agus luibheanna agus gach aon dath fén spéir orthu – pinc ós na ramháin, buí ós na méireanna Muire agus gorm ón dúán caoirigh.

'Thar aon bhláth eile is í seo a chuireann an áit seo i gcuimhne dhom nuair a bhím i bhfad uaidh,' arsa mise ag piocadh crobh de dúán caoirigh is mé ag déanamh iontais, mar a dheinim i gcónaí, dá dhath gorm. Bhí an lanntan ar a rabhamair breac-lan díobh. 'Sea, ta sé gann go maith in áiteanna eile,' arsa Adrian, ag aontú liom. 'Is bláth an-annamh í seo leis,' ar seisean ag cur a mhéir ar bhrobh de phóiríní deangáin a bhí ag gobadh amach idir chlocha an dúna.

'Póiríní seangain,' arsa mise, 'saxifrage a tugtar air i mBéarla.'

'Ní hea,' ar seisean, 'ach stonecrop'. A sheans aige-sin anois mise a cheartú.

'Bhuel as Laidin mar sin,' arsa mise gan an oiread san sásaimh a thabhairt dó. 'Ar ndóigh, tá an ceann eile acu "Saxifaga tridactlites" m 'ana chomónta anseo leis sa samhradh ach tá san imithe anois.'

'Sea, i dtús an Mheithimh a bhíonn sé sin amuigh.' Ba é ma shás é ó thaobh bláthanna fiáine dhó. Níor labhair sé arís go ceann i bhfad is níor labhras-sa ach an oiread. Bhí an triúr eile ag bladaráil leo, ag déanamh tuairimíochta i dtaobh an dúna, ag cur ceisteanna agus mise á bhfreagairt chomh maith agus a d'fheadfainn ach ar chuma éigin ní raibh suim ar bith agam ionntu. Ba chuma liom ná gliogarnach leanbh a raibh ar siúl acu. Air siúd, ar Adrian, a bhí m'aigne dírithe. B'ait liom é ach bhí a fhios agam gur dó siúd a bhí an teaspáinteas seo go léir ar siúl agam. Is leis siúd amháin a bhíos ag caint, dáiríre.

Ghaibheamar timpeall Cinn Sléibhe, agus nuair a thangamair i radharc na nOileán bhí gach 'Oh' agus 'Ah' as Martin taobh liom. Aon uair amháin eile a labhras le hAdrian go dtí go dtangamar go tigh Khruger. Éan dubh a bhí ag faoileáil timpeall os cionn barr na hAille Móire a thairg, 'áird.

'Sin í agat an' Chough,' arsa mise. 'Chuff' adúrt mar is mar sin a fuaimnítear é. 'Nó an préachán cos-dearg, mar a tugtar air as Gaeilge,' is mé ag caint le cách, mar dhea.

'An bhfacaís na cosa dearga,' arsa Adrian, ag lorg deimhniúcháin.

'N'fheaca an fhaid seo ó baile, mar tá giorra radhairc orm, ach is maith an chomartha air chomh maith imeall na sciathán air a bheith mantach faoi mar a bheadh na cleití ag imeacht uaidh ina leidhbeanna.'

Díreach ar an bpoinnte seo d'éirigh ceann eile acu in airde os comhair fhuinneog na cairte amach.

'Maith an áit a rabhais mar phréachán cosdearg,' arsa mise im' bholg.

Bhí ionadh ar i gceart an turas seo.

'Is an bhfuil a thuilleadh éanlaithe neamhchoitianta le fáil anseo timpeall?'

'Éanlaithe neamhchoitianta is ea iad ar fad, a bhuachaill, dá dtuigfeá a leath,' ach os ard,

'Bhuel, tá na héanlaithe mara ar na hoileáin – na guardail is na héin dearga is dá mbeifeá amuigh i mbád is mór an seó ar fad a radharc a chífeá ar éanlaithe ar nós an forcha is an chánóg bhán.'

'Is anseo ar a míntír?'

'Bhuel, ar bhóithre Chruach Mháthain is timpeall na Clasaí chífeá éan seilge éigin. Deinim amach gur seabhach gaoithe é ach ní bheinn ró-chinnte mar tá smuth mhaith caochshúilí orm.' Bhíos buailte aige, geall leis, gur chuimhníos 'is tá an 'stonechat' go coitianta leis 'Seaic a' Chaipín' mar a thugann na daoine timpeall air. Bhíos in amhras ar chreid sé in aon chor mé.

Bhraitheamair ná beadh aon díobháil ann deoch a dh'ól ar an bpoinnte seo is bá é tigh Khrugir a bhí oiriúnach chun é a dháil orainn. Is cé gur túisce deoch nó scéal do lean an chaint isteach sa bheár sinn. Bhíos ar eachtraí dhóibh ar Khruger, céarbh é is céarbh díobh é is na súáilcí a bhain lena phearsain. Chaitheamair seal ag féachaint ar na pictiúirí ar an bhfalla, go háirithe an ceann a bhfuil Kruger is Dev le feiscint in aonacht.

'Is furaist a dh'aithint gur in Árus an Uachtráin a thógadh an pictiúr seo.'

Arsa mise 'Canathaobh?'

'Mar d'aithneófá go maith gur Dev a bhí ag caint, agus Kruger ag éisteacht.'

'Is dána gach gadhair ar lic a tháirsigh féin,' arsa Niall.

'Is dána,' arsa mise, 'ar ndoigh Árus an Uachtaráin a thugaimísne i gcónaí ar an bpota seomra.'

B'fhada ó bheith fíor é seo, ach nach cuma, ní raibh ann ach slí chun an t-am a mheilt agus gáire a bhaint astu, rud a dhein sé.

'Gach ní mar is ceart, agus an pota seomra ar an ndriosúr,' a deireadáis leis le duine nach raibh ina bean tí ró-mhaith. Ach ós ag trácht ar photaí seomra atáimid, chualabhair, ar ndoigh, an rud a dúirt bean Khruger leis an bPoncánach mná,' arsa mise.

Bhí gach cluais ar bior.

'Bhuel, fadó fadó riamh, thiar ins na triocaidí, nuair nach raibh mórán trácht ar chairteacha mótair sa dúthaigh is gan móran acu feiscithe ach oiread do tháinig an Rolls Royce mór millteach seo, ar dhath na luaidhe, "Phantom", nó "Silver Cloud", nó rud éigin mar sin is dócha, bhuel do tháinig an mótar mór millteach seo timpeall Cheann Sléibhe is do stop sé ag tigh Khrugir is tháinig bean óg uasail amach as. "Is this Kruger's?" ar sise. Dúradh gurb ea, is más ea loirg sí lóistín na hoíche is do fuair sí é. Teaspáineadh na seomraí di is bhí sí sásta is cuireadh a cuid málaí suas 'on seomra.

'And now my good woman,' ar sise le Cáitín, bean Khrugir. 'Please direct me to the toilet.'

'Toilet?' arsa Cáitín. 'Toilet?' ar sise arís agus alltacht uirthi. 'What would we want a toilet for, dear, when we have the broad Atlantic.'

Ag an bpoinnte seo thosnaigh Niall agus Eibhlín agus mé féin ag caint ar staid na tíre seo agus na nithe atá á lot is conas mar a bhaineann polaitaíocht le gach ní anois is ná fuil aon 'fairplay' fágtha sa tsaol.

'Má bhí se riamh ann,' an t-aguisín a chuireas-sa féin leis an méid sin im' aigne. Thráchtamair ar scribhneóiri próis an Bhéarla in Éirinn ó Joyce is Brindley McNamara anuas go dtí an ghlúin atá anois ann is conas a chuireann siad go léir síos go minic ar an 'malaise' áirithe a chiallaíonn bheith Éireannach. Caint í seo a bhíonn ar siúl eatorthu féin ag Éireannaigh pé áit go mbíonn siad is nach suim le héinne ar bith é ach iad féin. Bhí a gcomhrá príomháideach ar siúl ag an mbeirt Shasanach i rith an ama seo, agus iad beag beann orainn-ne. N'fheadar an dtuigeann éinne go deo ach sin féinín féin conas go gcaitheann tagairtí gangaideacha do shagairt is d'easpaig, do mháithreacha Éireannacha is do mhná riallta teacht isteach i ngach cómhrá i dtaobh staid na tíre seo. Ní thuigimíd féin é, ach an oiread, tá an méid sin cinnte.

'Ó, drochthubaistí na staire atá á n-oibriú féin amach fós faoi ndeara an tír seo a bheith ina chocstaí,' arsa Niall, go húdarásach.

'Bhí sé ábhar bogaithe faoin am seo. Ní deirim ná go raibh deor faoin bhfiacal agam féin.'

'Sea, féach an taobh seo tíre, ar thit amach de thubaistí inti,' arsa mise, 'Is mór an ní ná fuil sí bán ar fad leis na céadta bliain, a bhfuil tárlaithe inti, ag cur Marú an Dúna san áireamh.' Bhí mo ghuth taréis éirí ard agus scréachach, mar a dheineann nuair a bhím ar deoch, mar d'fhéach Martin suas óna phiúnt leana duibhe agus d'fhéach Adrian suas óna phiúnt biotáille.

'Sea, Marú an Dúna,' arsa mise is mo ghuth ag éirí agus mé sa tsiúl arís go rábach an uair seo.

'Ceithre céad bliain is fiche ó shoin a thárla sé, níl ach cúpla míle suas an bóthar. Tháinig sé céad Spáinneach is Iodáileach i dtír chun cabhraithe leis an Gaeil, a bhí taréis éirí amach faoi Thiarna Deasmumhain. Tháinig Lord Grey de Wilton timpeall orthu ar thír, agus an t-Aimiréal Wynter ar muir, is cé gur gealladh anachal anama dóibh dúnmharaíodh gach mac máthar acu. Mar a scríobh Edmund Spencer ina pheannaireacht breá Íodálach. "Bands were sent in who forthwith fell to execution." Spencer a bhí in rúnaí ag Lord Grey ag an am agus féach go raibh sé ábalta ar an méid sin a scríobh gan crith nó freangadh ina láimh. Bhí an ghráin dhearg agam riamh ar Spencer is ar an bh"Faerie Queen", is féach go raibh an ceart ar fad agam.'

Má bhí searradh beag ciúin le braith ar mo cheathrar lucht éisteachta ní mise a thug aon toradh air ach leanúint ar aghaidh go dásachtach.

'Cuirtear an milleán de gnáth ar Denny, gurb é sin a bhí i gceannas na mbuíonta dúnmharaitheóirí ach deir muintir na háite gurb é Raleigh, an Sir

Walter clúiteach úd a leath a bhrat faoi chosa na banríona, a dhein an slad. Tá sé de nath i mbéal an phobail riamh ó shoin, má theastaíonn uathu scannradh a chur ar leanaí beaga ní gá dhóibh ará leó ach 'Cughat an púca Rálaí', 'Here's Raleigh, the boodyman'.

Bhí sórt craitheán oighearta le braith orthu fén am seo. Rud a chuir orm stad is féachaint ó dhuine go duine orthu.

Adrian a bhris an ciúineas suaithinseach.

'Well, I'm a Devonshire man myself, and Raleigh happens to be a local hero where I come from.'

Ó, a Dhé, anois a Mháire, tá an phraiseach ar fuaid na mias i gceart agat is do dhá spág mhóra sáite isteach go maith agat ann. Rith scata sean-fhocal timpeall mo mheamhrach in aonacht –

Is binn béal ina thost. Ia minic a bhris béal duine a shrón. Má shatalaíonn tú ar chac bó seanna leathnaíonn sé. Nuair a théann an gabhar an teampall ní stopann sé go haltóir. Bhí an ghaoth tógtha go maith as mo sheolta is ní mó adúrt arís go ceann tamaill. Ní gá dhom ará nár thugamair aon chuaird ar dhún san mí-ábhaireach úd an Óir.

Chuamair trí Riasc is tré Ghallarus is i gCill Mhaolcéadair trí chró na snáthaide. Thugas an gnáth-fháisnéis dóibh i dtaobh láithreáin luath-Chríostaíocha ach ní raibh mo chroí ann níos mó. Is maith ábalta a bhí Adrian taréis clabhsúr a chur orm i thiar i dtigh Khruger.

Ag teacht amach doras na Cille dhúinn bhí griain bhuí an tráthnóna ag taithneamh ar na goirt. Bhí scáillí fada ag titim ar fhraoch is ar raithneach na gcnoc is ar réimsí fada don bpréamh charraige a bhí tosnaithe cheana féin ag buíochtaint. Rith líne den dán a scríobh Seamus Heaney ar an radharc chéanna seo, geall leis, ó Ghallarus isteach im' cheann –

'And how he smiled at them as out they came,
The sea a censer and the grass a flame.'

Dúrt an dán dóibh, ceann des na foth-dhánta nua aimseartha sa Bhéarla a fhanann im' cheann ar chuma éigin. Ba dhóigh leat gur paidir a bhí a rá agam, bhíomair go léir chomh ciúin, is nuair a bhí an dán ráite bhí mar a bheadh oscailteacht nua tagtha ar mo chroí. D'fhéach soir ar fhothrach na seanamhainistreach mar a mbíodh cónaí ar na manaigh fadó is bhail sé isteach im cheann nárbh aon díobháil dul ag féachaint ar Bheistí na Glas Gaibhneach. D'fhiafraíos den gceathrar ar mhaith leo aon rud amháin eile a fheiscint. Bhíodar sásta. D'fhiafríodar cad a bhí ann.

'Beistí na Glas Gaibhneach,' arsa mise, ón bhféachaint a fuaireas thuigeas go gcaithfinn ainm na bó a aistriú go Béarla dóibh is an scéal go léir a insint ó thús. Conas mar a bhí bó iontach dárb ainm An Glas Ghaibhneach ann aon uair amháin. Conas gur bó chomh bainniúil san ab ea í gur chuma cén soitheach a chuirthí fúithi go líonadh sí suas é. Conas gur thrialladar í a chrú isteach i dtubán is fós gur líon sí é is gur tháinig sí arís tráthnóna is bhí a húth chomh hathtaithe sin le teann bainne amhail is nach raibh aon tubán in aon chor fúithi ar maidin. Conas gur chrúigh an bhean áirithe seo sa deireadh isteach i gcriathar í is gur thál an bhó ar feadh an lae is sa deireadh gur chas sí a ceann is nuair a chonaic sí a cuid bainne go léir ag rith síos ar fuaid an fhána ón gcriathar gur thóg sí a ceann is gur imigh sí ón mbean ag snámh amach sa bhfarraige is nuair a bhí sí amuigh sa bhfarraige cúpla céad slat ón dtráigh gur ligh sí aon ghéim amháin is ba uile na dúthaí, a bhí síolraithe uaithi féin, gur leanadar isteach sa bhfarraige í is ghur shnamhadar leo amach is nár fhéacathas aon radharc ar aon bhó acu beo nó marbh ó shoin i leith.

'Beistí Ba Bhréannain', a thugann cuid des na daoine ar an áit,' arsa mise, agus deir siad gur duine des na manaigh a chrúigh an bhó isteach sa chriathar.

'Braitheann sé is dócha an ar fhear nó ar bhean a theastaíonn uait an milleán a chur i dtaobh imeacht na bó báine is peaca an tSínsir is ar ruagairt an chéadlá ón gáirdín.' Anois a bhí an ceart aige.

Chuamair síos an bóithrín ciúin chun na mainistreach. Bhí an bóithrín cúng go maith is bhí duilleoga crainn agus bláthanna fiúise á chlúdach isteach ar gach taobh. Bhí foth-bhláth dos na méiríní púca nach raibh fós feoite is theaspáineas don gcomhluadar conas a chuirimís ar ár méaranna iad is sinn inár leanaí is go dtugaimís 'méaracáin' orthu. Conas a dheinimís siogarlaínní des na bláthanna fiúise chomh maith, ag crochadh péirí acu óna gcluasa is conas a dheinimís an mhíl a shúraic astu.

D'fhiafraigh Niall ciall an fhocail 'beiste'.

'Sórt tubán mór éadoimhin adhmaid is ea beiste,' adúrtsa. 'Is ann a cuirthí an bainne chun go dtiocfadh an t-uachtar ar barra. 'Ní scríobhfaidh a scilléidín íochtar an bheiste,' adeirtí nuair a phósadh cailín iseach i dtigh go raibh bun maith faoin muintir ann. N'fhéacas-sa ceann lem' linn mar tá an t-uachtarlann tagtha le fada ach chonac pictiúirí dóibh.'

'Agus conas go bhfeicfimídne iad mar sin,' arsa Eibhlín, 'go raibh smut den gligín ag roinnt léi.'

'Á, ní haon ghnáth-bheistí na cinn seo ach bullán mór graoi cloiche go bhfuil poill éadoimhne ann in aice a chéile is go gcuirtear le beistí iad. Tá cloch den sórd sin feicthe agaibh, ní foláir, ar Shráid Mhór an Daingin, an ceann ar a dtugann siad an "Holy Stone". Bullán an téarma seandálaíochta a bhaineann lena leithéid agus baineann sé de ghnáth le láithreáin luath-Chríostaíochta.'

Bhí a fhios agam go maith go raibh an chloch a bhí uaim sa tarna gort taobh thiar den sean-mhainistir. Siar linn á cuardach. Shiúlaíomar gach órlach den gort ach má dhein, bhí sé folach.

'B'fhéidir gur dhá gort suas atá sí,' arsa mise. D'imíomair linn agus chuardaíomair an dá ghort san chomh maith ach tásc ná tuairisc ar na beistí chéana ní raibh le feiscint. Bhíos ag éirí mí-shuaimhneach faoin am seo.

'Tá siad dhá gort síor, más buan mo chuimhne.'

Ach níor bhuan, mar ní raibh aon rian dóibh ansan ach oiread.

'B'fhéidir go bhfuil sí clúdaithe le caonach. B'fhéidir go bhfuil an gort domhain-treafa acu is cré curtha anáirde air. B'fhéidir go bhfuil sí árdaithe as an áit ag JCB éigin.'

Bhíos suaite go maith faoin am seo. Éinne a d'fhéachfadh anuas orainn ó mhullach an chnoic déarfaidíst go rabhamair glan as ár meabhar. Cúigear againn ag póirseáil timpeall i ngort agus ceathrar den gcúigear sin is iad ag tóraíocht a ngadhar is gan fios a dhatha acu, ach go raibh seanchloch éigin i ngort éigin in áit éigin am éigin. Mise ba mheasa ar fad acu is mé ag rith suas is síos, soir agus siar gan stop ná staonadh mar bhíos siúiráilte go raibh aon chloch ann – nach raibh sí feicthe agam na blianta fada ó shoin nuair a bhíos im' leanbh. D'fhéadfainn an leabhar a thabhairt go raibh an chloch dhá gort soir ón sean-mhainistir ach dá bhfaighinn Éire air ní fhéadfainn teacht uirthi.

Adrian ba thúisce gur tháinig ciall chuige. Shuigh sé faoi bhun claí teorainn uachtaraigh na ngort beag is a dhá spanndla fada coise sínte roimhe amach. Las sé suas toitín da dhéantús féin is thosnaigh ag baint gail as. Bhí radharc álainn síos uaidh – Cuan brea leathan Ard na Caithne ó thuaidh is an grian ag dul faoi thiar i nDunChaoin is riastraí fada dearg á caitheamh fan na spéire aici. Bhí uisce an chuain ar nós pána gloine is dathanna na spéire á frith-chaitheamh aici. Báid bheaga iascach ar snámh innti. Ceann Sibéal agus na Trí Deirféireacha is iad chomh grámhar maisiúil le haon ainmhithe mánla ina luí faoi dhraíocht an tráthnóna. Cé déarfadh go mbeidíst chomh fíochmhar sin lá gaoithe go raibh paidir faoi leith ag na daoine ina gcoinne –

'Go gcumhdaí Dia sin ar an bhFiach is a Mháthair
Ar an mBinn Beag is ar an mBinn Mhéanach
Is ar Bhinn Diarmada na bhFiacla Gránna.'

Ach bhí cuma chomh suaimhneach anois ar an dúthaigh timpeall. Dob fhéidir leat an suaimhneas a chlos ag titim ón spéir ina deor deor mar a dúirt file an Bhéarla i dtaobh Inis Fraoigh.

'Is álainn ar fad an dúthaigh é,' arsa Adrian, nuair a shuíos síos ina thaobh ar deireadh. Fear tuisceannach ab ea é ina dhiaidh sin is uile, a cheapas agus ar feadh aon nóiméad amháin do bhraitheas an-chóngarach dó.

'Is cad a dheineann tú sa gheimhreadh?' ar seisean liom is sinn ag siúl síos go dtí Martin is an bheirt eile is sinn ag bogadh i dtreó na gcairteacha.

'Ó, tá mo chuid oibre agam is tugann san an-shásamh dom is coimeadann sé sa tsiúl mé mar más dóigh le héinne go bhfuil sé furaist Frainncís agus Matamataic a dhingeadh isteach i gceannaibh cailíní meánscoile, tá breall mór orthu.'

'Ní hiné a bhí i gceist agam, ach cad a dheineann tú lasmuigh ded' chuid oibre?'

'Bíonn foth-phionnt agam amuigh lem' chairde anois is arís is cathaim an-chuid ama ag léamh.'

'Deinim amach gur saol an-uaigneach é,' ar seisean.

'Bhuel, is dócha gurb ea, don té ná tuigfeadh,' arsa mise, 'ach tá sásamh le fáil agam sa taobh-seo tíre nach raibh riamh agam i gCathair Londain, ná i mBaile Áth Cliath. Tá sásamh an tseanchais is na scéalta agam.'

'Is a gcreideann tú iontu, mar scéalta?' ar seisean.

Tuigeadh dom gur míbhéasach í mar cheist.

'Bhuel, ní hea go gcreidim iontu focal ar fhocal, ach creidim sa rud atá taobh thiar díobh.'

'Agus cén rud é sin?'

'Ní fhéadfainn ará, ach is dóigh liom gur . . .'

'I gcead duit, ach is dóigh liomsa nach gcreideann tú a dhóthain iad, sin í an trioblóid atá ort. "Alienation" iomlán atá ort. Féach an slí nach rabhais ábalta ar theacht ar na beistí sin ó chianaibh, dá mhéid do chuid seanchais orthu.'

Bhuel, a leithéid de mhasla taréis mise a bheith ag déanamh leidhb óinsí díom féin feana tráthnóna á theaspáint timpeall! Is dócha nach gceapann siad go bhfuil luid faoin spéir le déanamh agamsa ach ag déanamh seó bóthair díom féin ar mhaithe lena leithéid.

D'fhágas slán le mo cheathrar go gairid ina dhiaidh sin agus d'imíos abhaile dom féinín féin. D'áitíodar orm teacht leo chun deoch a bheith againn le chéile ach d'eitíos glan dóibh. Go hobann bhíos taréis éirí an-chortha dóibh. Cad ina thaobh go raghainn in aon áit le dream a bhí chomh lán suas díobh féin is a cheap gur acu féin amháin a bhí fios fátha an aonscéil, gan trácht ar na carraigreacha Béarla. 'Alienation', ambaist, is dócha gur as barr a chinn amach a chaith sé an focal sin is go raibh iontas air nuair a thuigeas é in aon chor. 'Alienation', ambaist, sin carraig duit agus is dócha gur cheap sé ná tuigfinn é, agus gan ionnam ach bean tuaithe, agus bean Ghaeltachta ina theannta san. Is dóigh leis, is dócha, nach mbíonn aon fhonn ar ár leithéidí taisteal, nó cead ár gcos a bheith againn chomh maith lena dhream féin, dream tógála na h-Impireachta. Ná bíonn aon chur amach againn ar aon ní lasmuigh de oileáinín iathghlas na hÉireann. Bhuel i gcead dó agus na coda dar díobh é, do bhíos-sa tráth in áiteanna go mbeadh eagla ar a leithéid sin a chraiceann rós-gheal a loscadh le dul ann, is ní mise amháin a shiúl an domhain ach na mílte a bhí romham. Nó cad deirir leo siúd a chuaigh do Butte, Montana, nó go dtí Van Diemen's Land. Cuimhnigh ar na Conneries, nár tháinig abhaile ó New South Wales ó shoin, dá méid paidreacha a dúradh ar a son le linn an Aifrinn. Cuimhnigh ar an Spailpín Fánach agus ar 'Amhrán na Mianach', is an fear bocht a chaith blianta dá shaol faoi thalamh gan faic le feiscint aige

'ach mo sholaisín caol ar mo hata ar maidin le fáinne an lae.'

'Alienated,' ab ea, bhuel má tá féin ná raibh maith aige as é a rá chomh neamhbhalbh liom. Is cad mar gheall ar an mbuachaill úd ó Chaisléan na Mainge a chuir an scanradh go léir ar mhuintir na hAstráile –

'There was a Wild Colonial Boy, Jack Duggan was his name.'

Mór an ní nach raibh a leithéid anseo anois mar is doilig a bhí scannradh maith ag teastáil ó chuid des na daoine na laethanta seo, i dteannta le leasú maith a bheith ag teastáil óna dtóinte . . .

Bhíos cúpla uair' chloig ag siúl síos suas ar an gcuma sin ar fuaid an tí go dtí gur thainig sánas orm is gur thit mo chodhladh orm sa deireadh. An rud deireannach gur chuimhníos air sarar thit mo chodladh orm ná 'Alienation' ambaist.

Is mé á scríobh seo táim ag féachaint amach an fhuinneog ar chuan breá leathan-aoibhinn Fionntrá. Tá gainéad ag tomadh is ag éirí. N'fheadar ná gurb é an gainéad chéanna a bhí ann an lá eile. Táim ag cuimhneamh gan stop ar an rud sin adúirt Adrian –

'Ar ndóigh is é an trioblóid atá ortsa, ná creideann tú do dhóthain ins na scéalta.' É sin agus an rud adúirt sé mar gheall ar uaigneas a bheith orm i rith an gheimhridh. Ar ndóigh, níl aon teora le fámaire fada fionn de Shasanach chun an scéal a thabhairt duit gan aon fhiacal a chur ann. Díreach ar nós an slataire caol ard de Shasanach gur chaitheas trí bliana dem shaol ina theannta is ná dúirt liom ar deireadh ach 'So long, luv, it was good while it lasted,' is é ag tabhairt cúl na láimhe dhom, is é ag feadaíl is é ag gabháilt amach an doras dó féin. Uaigneas, goidé uaigneas! Ná fuil Con Crithir agam, nach bhfuil Caol Mac Cruimhthain is an Ghlas Ghaibhneach agam. Nach bhfuil Crom Dubh is Mis ar bharra gach sléibhe agam. Nach bhfuil an préachán cos-dearg is Seaic a' Chaipín agam. Nach bhfuil na méiríní púca is na póirínní seangáin agam. Nach bhfuil an dúthaigh leathan álainn seo de Dhuibhneacha agam chomh fada soir le TráLí. Uaigneas, goidé uaigneas, adeirim.

Barry White Stole My Wife
Jack Murray

The first, the last, my everything,
And the answer to, all of my dreams,

Cathy lay in bed, restless, staring at the ceiling and listening to the CD alarm clock, but she wanted to close her eyes and fall effortlessly into a dream; not an ordinary dream, but one with a Barry White soundtrack, where she would be ravished by a dark romantic lover in a white suit; a lothario made to give, and give, and keep giving.

She pulled the quilt tight and sunk deeper into the pillow, closing her eyes with concentration in an attempt to stave off the morning and re-enter blanket street.

'Hi. Are you awake, my love?'

Her efforts were in vain and the moment was lost. Barry White was now a pipe dream and the outside world outside would soon have to be faced.

'Well, I'm awake now, Declan,' she said.

'I just thought with the CD alarm having come on and all, you'd have woken up.'

'Well, maybe you should have thought a bit harder.'

'Jesus, Cathy, what is eating you?'

The truth was always Declan's problem; it would stare him in the face and he wouldn't see it. He couldn't see anything much unless it was through his self-centred vision of the world.

His office party was on the night just passed and he arrived home very late, seven a.m. to be exact, and now their en-suite master bedroom stank of stale alcohol. For the longest time Cathy denied he had a drink problem, because admitting it was more than she could deal with. He wasn't a fall-down-drunk, slurred-speech alcoholic, but was liable to cause severe embarrassment to himself, and anyone in his company, after consuming more than three consecutive drinks.

'What time did you make it back from the office party last night?'

'I'm not sure, maybe three or four. What's that got to do with anything? Isn't it only on once a year?'

Yes, it was only on once a year and when most people go to their office party they cut loose and let their hair down. Sometimes colleagues get a little shocked, because they have never seen this alternative side in the sedate surroundings of the office. But Declan's situation was a little different. He had got home at seven a.m. because he was having an affair with his personal assistant, Gillian, and because he went back to her apartment in Temple Bar after the party had finished.

'I'll tell you what's wrong with it, Declan. You should have called me last night to let me know you were going to be late. You know I'm a light sleeper and the last time I checked the clock it was well after three or four.'

Declan was always very clever with his deception. He only ever slept over at Gillian's when Cathy was away, or when he was supposed to be down the country on business. In truth he knew going back to Gillian's after the party was stupid and risky on the night of the Christmas party.

He had thought about ringing home but he was too drunk and knew it would be impossible to lie and sound credible then. His mind was blank and he couldn't remember what happened at the party or what he had done. He knew there'd been dancing; he loved dancing and boy, could Gillian move. But that was all he could recall, everything else was a haze.

'Is that all that is worrying you, Cathy? Come on, turn over and I'll give you a spoon hug. We'll forget about it and it'll be OK.'

His words were spoken more in hope than in confidence. In Declan's eyes a spoon hug was the treatment prescribed to heal any relationship problem. He would snuggle in behind Cathy, wrap himself behind her slender frame and gently kiss her back. It didn't matter how bad the misdemeanour perpetrated, a spoon hug would cure it. He only ever used it with Cathy and would have recognised his cheapness if he ever shared it with other women.

'I don't want a stupid spoon hug, Declan, we were supposed to be doing jobs on the house today and look at yourself, you're in no fit state to go anywhere. You could hardly go to the toilet now without getting a speed wobble.'

Their home was badly in need of some care and attention. It hadn't been painted in a few years and the garden, his domain, was completely overgrown. He had agreed to go to the garden centre today to buy new hedge plants and flowers and to help Cathy to pick out a new sofa and bathroom tiles. It was supposed to be a day of domestic bliss, and right now the way he felt he would rather lie face down on a bed of nails than get out of bed.

'What do you mean, Pet? I'm perfectly fine and I am actually really looking forward to going shopping. In fact I was talking to Gillian in the office the other day and she was saying that ocean marine is the new colour this season. Maybe we could get the tiles in that colour.'

It wasn't like he had any clue about tiles or colours, but he was doing his best to paper over the cracks and rescue a normal weekend from the ashes of his Friday debauchery. He thought if he mentioned her in conversation as Gillian from the office it would normalise the situation; he often used this trick when he was sleeping with someone from the office. Then if he ever had a slip of the tongue, or the slightest suspicion, he could get away with it.

'Yes, Declan, ocean marine is a great colour. I was reading about it in Image Style from last month, maybe Gillian saw it there.'

As she lay there with Saturday morning sleep lingering in her eyes, she got an overwhelming urge to confront Declan's lies. She'd repressed her feelings too long, to preserve their marriage, but now she'd had enough.

She wanted to look into his eyes and tell him that she knew all about Gillian from the office, his twenty-two-year-old blonde secretary, who he'd been sleeping with for months. She wanted to know was she better than Samantha, or Catherine, or Deborah, the one he was sleeping with last year from the UK subsidiary.

She turned her gaze away from her bedside locker and towards Declan for the first time. Their faces were inches apart.

'Do you know what I really want to know?' she enquired.

'What, Love,' he asked nervously.

'Is that spoon hug still on the agenda?'

Cathy turned over, reset Barry White on the CD player, and Declan moved his warm arm around her. She closed her eyes and tried again to block out the outside world and to dream.

You're my sun, my moon, my guiding star,
My kind of wonderful, that's what you are.

Assignation
Emily Maher

She felt more human with her high heels on,
a slick of lipstick and a cigarette.
Ammunition rendered pearly pink,
straight off the catwalks of Milan.

Down the wine and out the door,
kids whooping, swinging, cackles of
innocent glee let loose as she made her way
to another assignation in a darkened bar.

Hours later, strange surroundings melt
into nights of different faces.
Discarded garments languish on a chair,
earlier passion distilled in crumples, how he'd yelled

that name, not hers. But never mind.
Another notch on some poor stag's bed
is nothing to cry over, just spilled milk.
The foghorn's low call echoes; she mouths goodbye.

Picture Imperfect
Emily Maher

To flee the rat race.
Get away from all the hustle-bustle.
Live my dreams.

To be near the sun and the sea, to throw away my watch,
drink wine at noon and have an affair with a butcher –
just look at his hands, that smile!

To sip black coffee till dusk,
all of these were my secret dreams
and they did not include you.

I huddled beside an oil-filled radiator,
wheeled it religiously from damp kitchen
to sitting room to cramped, tiny bedroom.

We weren't happy, you and me.
Your big heart crushed me. So I ran away.
Too weak for real life. Too weak for you.

Your letters ask if I'm okay? You care too much.
I'm fine. Stop writing letters to my mother's house.
I live a different life these days.

Uncouple
Emily Maher

Tonight you will simulate being
happy and content with life;
while I, eyes closed, dream of life undone,
embroidery delicately unpicked.

In the morning we will trace our steps
again across the duvet landscape;
broach the breach that's growing there,
beside the pillow and under my hair.

Lying rigid, hardly daring to touch,
we will couple and uncouple for the last time.

That Night
Emily Maher

That night I met you for a friendly drink.
We talked for hours, drank wine, I fell asleep.
You thought this cute or sweet or some such term.
The barman disagreed. He threw us out.

I almost tripped; you laughed. These moments make up
life; single memories suspended in a
vacuum of lust and too much wine to drink.
Your hand grasped mine for fear I'd fall again.

And who'd have thought we two would find a place
despite real life's demands on soul and head.
This place of secret moments that we've shared;
of talking late at night in coffee bars.

Your head droops low, hands cup latte. Eyelids flicker
and say hello again after all these years.

Meditation on a Lost Evening
Emily Maher

I thought it started with the champagne. You slammed your fist on the table and declared that champagne was the only thing for it. I was delighted.

Later, when there was no more champagne, you said we should get a taxi. So I said yes and we did. We got a taxi to your place. And it was good in the taxi. And I could tell it would be good at your place.

Much later, when it was almost getting bright again, I said that I'd go, would you call me a taxi? You were sitting on the bed, half turned away from me. And you twisted your head and looked at me. That's when it really started.

You twisted your head and you looked at me with disgust. You stood up, walked over to the other side of the bed. You sat down and started kissing me. At first it was nice, the way it had been earlier I suppose. But then you grabbed my wrist tightly and held it on the bed and your tongue seemed to bore into my mouth and it was hard to breathe. And then you were on top of me. And you know the rest.

You fell asleep afterwards. Too much champagne and beer and cheap Chardonnay at dinner. Pathetic. So in the half-light of the morning I retrieved my shoes and skirt, I got dressed and I left the apartment. Outside, it was cold. I kind of sort of knew where I was, so I started walking towards town.

And so, of course, I will probably never see you again. Not for a long time. I think this as I sit in the waiting room watching daytime television, a chat show, on the screen in the corner. Some woman has just met her long-lost brother. They embrace. The receptionist calls my name and I go to the hatch. She gives me a form to fill out. Insurance.

And in a while I am called to go to the doctor's room. It's a lady doctor; she's young, my age. Her white coat has a coffee stain on the sleeve. She looks tired. There are the usual 'healthy-living' questions – drinking, smoking, do I have a boyfriend? Of course, he's at work. You know, he's busy right now. The condom split.

I've taken the tablet. I went to the public toilet under the stairs in the shopping centre. The one that's always cold. And I've taken it. So it's over. Last night is finally over. Today is here.

I am sitting in the café, the new flashy one that serves hazelnut cappuccino and paninis with goat's cheese and sun-dried tomato pesto. It's lunchtime. Office worker wide boys are squaring up to each other while their female counterparts surreptitiously check their make-up in the chrome counter top. I know. I've done it so many times before.

I only took the morning off work. Said I had a meeting with the bank manager.

I'd pre-planned this excuse as I had a feeling last night would be worthy of an extra hour or two in bed dreaming of someone new. Pity it wasn't.

It should have been perfect. A charity ball in the most exclusive hotel in town. Fake tan, blow-dried hair, new outfit. Italian stilettos with diamante detailing. Perfect. And in a way it was perfect for most of the evening. Until I saw that look in your eye, as if you were about to get sick. It made my stomach turn to see such hate directed towards me. And then it didn't matter because you were hurting me so much I could no longer think. I'm still sore – my wrists and jaw are aching. You did that. To me. You did that to me on the night that should have been perfect, almost was perfect.

So I go to the office. And I sit at my desk in some semblance of contributing to the overall corporate goal of the organisation. But really I am just thinking how I lost an evening so easily. How I could have been so careless. It wasn't even the wine. I didn't have too much, never do. I'd feel sick.

It had to be perfect, this evening. Somehow, after all the beauty treatments and prodding and poking, after the eyeliner and the blusher, after the fake nails, somehow, as I sit here and stare out the window, and my colleagues get on with pushing paper and making deals, somehow I realise I am lost. And really it's not your fault that I'm lost. Not your fault that it feels like I'm floating above the office, looking down on them all as they respond to personal e-mails and draw up pointless spreadsheets. It had to be perfect. So I ran after you, ran after a connection. And it's ended up like this, ended up that I have my head in my hands and I've never felt so empty before. Never before in my short life.

Maybe I owe you an explanation? Maybe none of it was your fault. I should have stayed the night, shouldn't have said I was going home. You must have felt I was pushing you away. When really I was hoping you'd suggest we get together for a drink, a meal, a chat sometime. That's all I wanted. A chat sometime. Is that too much to ask? Is it? Perhaps.

And that seems to be my problem. I expect too much. I want the large bucket of popcorn when the medium would be more than enough. I suppose you could call it greed. And that's how it was with you last night. I wasn't ready to go home. And I saw you on the other side of the room, vaguely knew you from the scene, and I went over to your table and sat down and said hello. And that's when it started. When you mentioned the champagne. And that's when I was hooked. For better or worse. Although now, now that it's all over, it was clearly for worse. But I'm just too greedy to have realised that in time. And this is my punishment.

So I sit at my desk and think about all this and wonder will it ever be the same again? Will I ever go to one of those parties again, with the girls dressed up like little dolls and the boys huddled at the bar gesticulating and guffawing and everyone pretending they'd rather be somewhere else, when really they can't quite believe their luck to be there. Those events with the same faces, the same conversations, the same scandals.

And the answer, of course, is no. Because I've realised it was the shiny veneer that attracted me. The shiny veneer that is nothing more than a thin gossamer film covering what's underneath the surface. How was I ever so taken in by it all? How did I think there was something worthwhile going on at those parties? I suppose I have you to thank for that little blinding flash of insight, that light-bulb eureka moment. I knew there was jealousy. I knew there was rivalry. But I never knew there was hate. Never knew it till I saw it in your eyes last night.

So I suppose that's the heart, the crux, the centre. I can't thank you for what you did. It could have been worse, I suppose, but I can't thank you. What you did to me last night, those words you said, the way you held my wrists so tight I thought I would faint, the venom in your eyes when your elbow met my jaw, I won't forget any of that. But I'm thankful it happened, no matter how perverse that sounds. All of it. Because I have an escape route now. An escape route from this world. And maybe one day you'll be thankful too. Because you can always find some sliver of positivity, some glimpse of hope, some reason to keep going.

There isn't much more to say. Isn't much more to think really. And as I leave the office, put on my coat in the hall, hail a taxi on the street, there's nothing left to regret either. It happened. You won't get away with it. I've heard all the stories about the shame of reporting something like this. And I won't be one of those non-statistics. Won't let you drift into the shadows ready to do it all over again. And again.

So that's where we stand, you and I. One lost evening later and both our lives will shortly be immeasurably altered. And you're probably in some bar drinking, gulping the talent, hoping to get lucky again tonight. And perhaps you will. And perhaps the day will come, in twenty years' time, when I see you on the street, or in a shop, or across a bar, perhaps the day will come when I can understand or forgive or rationalise. But perhaps that day will never come to pass. If it does, even if it doesn't, we'll never get the evening back, you and I. We'll never hold in our hearts collective memories, good memories, memories of drinking champagne in a hotel bar at midnight. And you in a tuxedo. And me in a puffy skirt and diamond earrings. And the two of us smiling.

Because they are lost, those memories. Lost like you and lost like me. Lost with the evening, lost.

Opportunity Lost
Iain Wilkinson

'I appreciate this is very hard for you to accept but I must repeat the urgency and importance of having the procedure. As quickly as possible. There really is no medical reason to delay or postpone it, though I understand you may wish to give yourself a brief time to perhaps arrange to store some for future purposes.'

Alex stared across the desk and wondered whether the doctor could be persuaded to just shut up. I understand what you are saying. I understand why you are saying it. I understand the urgency. I don't need to be repeatedly told the bloody obvious. I want some time to digest this. I cannot contemplate this right now. Give me the information so I can make a balanced decision.

'OK, I get it, I understand what you're saying and while it's an enormous shock I will do what's necessary of course. But I have to have a short time at least to absorb the news. Tell me simply and concisely, just the basic facts please. I understand your concerns; what sort of time could I delay this without causing irreparable damage? Can I hold off for a week or a month, say? Two months?'

The doctor sat forward. 'Cancer will spread. It's already in both of your testicles but as far as we can tell nowhere else yet. Every day you carry infected tissue in your body increases the risk that the infection will spread to some other part of your body. I cannot tell you categorically that if you wait a week then you have a fifty per cent chance of it spreading or if you wait two weeks then it is a racing certainty. What I can tell you is that you should not take risks with this because the time you wait may be enough for the infection to spread. It could then kill you. If we remove the testicles now, tomorrow, the day after, we are taking the best preventative action we possibly can.'

Alex stared back. No help there then. Both balls, no option but to take them and leave him impotent for the rest of his life. Impotent. Alex didn't get much sex but he'd always been hopeful. The doctor was twittering on about sperm donation and freezing, should he wish to have children in the future. Alex was picturing the conversation he'd have to have with a prospective partner long before there'd be any need for a turkey baster. Who in her right mind would get past a third or fourth date when she realised he couldn't perform? Even if he found such an extraordinary or desperate woman would he want to lie beside her every night knowing that he wanted her but was incapable of performing? Would he have to wield a dildo? Offer to hold her vibrator? Wear, for the love of god, a strap-on?

'I need to go out and think and walk around or something. I'll call you tomorrow and we can make arrangements but today I have to leave and be given some time. OK?'

Alex left the office with a promise to call the next day, walked through the waiting area where the line of faces raised to examine his for the reassurance of another's misery, almost fell on his way down the stairs and bashed through the doors into the car park. You see, whatever about the future of his sex life, Alex had a problem with his past. It was inadequate. He didn't have the history to be able to say 'at least I've had a good run' or 'good thing I'd shagged fifty women'. He started to count. Audrey, Elaine, Susannah – technically he'd never actually had penetration with Susannah but on the other hand he had ejaculated somewhere on or around her, so she counted – Aine, Catherine – another no penetration but this list was about testicles not virginity – and Maria. That was it. Six. His sum total of sexual partners in thirty years or thereabouts of puberty and adulthood. Six women he'd ever been naked with, six that had put their hands on him, six that had let him return the favour, just four who he'd actually had intercourse with and just two who'd offered oral pleasures. What kind of a list was that to console him for the rest of his life?

In the car he slammed the door and rammed the key in the ignition. This wasn't a joke, his balls would be toast in just a couple of days and he had nothing to show for the first thirty years of having them in full working order. Was he abnormal, could he not have made more of an effort? He had just a single solitary one-night stand to count in his sad list of six. One. Shit sex too. The number of nights he'd stood in bars eyeing up the talent and bottled it. Just think the sort of count he'd have if he'd just had the balls, pun not lost on him, to go and ask. Even on a five per cent success rate he'd have added at least twenty more to the list. Who knows, he might have become immune to rejection. There was no doubt the practice would have done him some good, added a little longevity to his performance, maybe taken the novelty value away and made each act a little less anxious. Twenty might have become forty, he'd have met other women through some of those women. There might have been threesomes, sisters, twins for god's sake. Why had he never even had the inspiration for a fantasy about a pair of twins, or a threesome of triplets. Probability surely should have been on his side; there must have been twins along the way that he'd just stepped past without a comment. Couldn't think of any though.

He drove distractedly through the hospital grounds and onto the street. Realistically, he thought, I have a week to work with here. Take a chance on leaving the damn things in for one week. In that week if I had a girlfriend I could have sex maybe four times a day every day, twenty-eight times in the week. Allowing for a few bursts of energy make it thirty times. Thirty more times wouldn't be bad but without a willing girlfriend it would be impossible. Even if he met someone in the next hour who liked him it might take a few days to get her in bed and even then she'd hardly agree to shack up continuously for a week. Of course this is all nonsense, complete rubbish. He's dying, maybe already terminally ill and he's worrying about getting laid. All logic said clearly and concisely to have the damn things removed and get on with living a full life. Put some sperm in storage just in case you want kids some day and then let the surgeon do his thing. How bad will it be to have no urges any more? No more sitting up late watching a film in case the actress gets her top off, no more dropping into so-called cutting edge soft porn flicks on the pretence of being a connoisseur, no more watching daft reality shows hoping the women get topless. He could listen to music, learn to play the guitar, get fit, run marathons, go back to college. So many things to do with a new lease of life. Be easier to run with less weight, less kit to pack into the shorts for his marathons and triathlons. Not that he was in the habit of running of course. Whatever his resolution before the surgery he knew well that post-surgery he'd settle into a funk on the sofa with occasional flashbacks to enthusiasm. It's like a reformed drug addict burning flab and getting a little rush from the deposits left by the munchies during a long-forgotten trip. It'll be just another reminder of his inadequacies, as though he needed one.

He was now parked just off Mespil Road looking at a woman standing beneath a tree. A woman who was surely a prostitute, hopefully a prostitute. Her head turned slowly from side to side and her skirt was pretty short, at least for this weather. This could be embarrassing if she wasn't. The line he was running through his head was 'Excuse me, I need to spend a week with you. A full week in my apartment. Food, drink, everything provided as long as we can have sex as often as it suits me. How much would you charge for that?' He wonders if he should say 'excuse me' like some saddo. Maybe Johns – he'd be a John shortly – didn't use polite chit chat. Probably they were gruff and businesslike, no nonsense, no sign of uncertainty. Get in, do this, go there, take that, don't talk. Nice image in his head though, sitting up in bed as the woman returned from the bathroom naked and willing to go again. They could learn about each other's lives, get pally, maybe he could help her off the game. There was a cosy future here for them both, except that his balls would be gone. Still, some memory. A new image emerged in his little fantasy factory. Years down the road men would struggle to look him in the eye when he admitted to being a castrato – Jesus there's a thought, would he turn into some kind of soprano? – until he explained that the first thing he did when he found out was get a whore and bang her till she bled for the whole week leading up to the operation. He'd describe the penultimate blow job in the car park of the hospital. He'd explain how the whore had gone to his room and given him another after the hot young nurse had shaved his unquenchable crotch. They'd laugh and clap him on the back, he's a bloke they'd say, quite a man. No different from them, a man's man through and through. Empty scrotum aside.

She's no looker though, a bit rough and ready. Fag as well, Alex hates the taste of cigarette smoke. She might want to smoke after sex all week long, then she'll want to go out for fags and she mightn't come back. On top of that his neighbours would then see a right slapper wandering in and out for a week. It might be funny to regale roomfuls of men with the story in a couple of months' time but he didn't want neighbours talking about him. People wouldn't understand this and he certainly didn't need to start some sort of debate on the subject. Maybe a rough slapper wasn't the right answer, or maybe a hotel would be better. Hotels are bloody expensive though and he didn't have as much as a toothbrush with him. Best to go home and pack a bag, maybe even drive to some other town and do it there. Better to avoid possible complications. Another town means having to find the local kerb-crawling area, not necessarily the easiest thing. Who could he ask? A policeman? A taxi driver?

He started the engine and pulled away, looking again at the woman – she definitely was a prostitute in that outfit – in the mirror. She was rough as an old boot now he looked, not at all the sort of farewell he wanted to give to his nads. He needed some quality or at the very least he was prepared to settle for some variety. Time to go up-market, he thought. There's got to be some sort of escort agency around a city this size. So he stopped at a newsagents and bought the listings magazines they had. These things were notorious for carrying advertisements for that sort of thing. Plenty of euphemisms, but the ads were right up his street. Not that you could be sure that you were definitely getting some hottie of course. 'Beautiful Russian Blondes', 'Asian Wonders', 'Black Beautys' – he couldn't forgive the misspell so avoided that one – they were all here. Time to find a call box, might be better not to use his own mobile.

'Eh, hello, yes. I was wondering if you could give me a rough idea of how much it might be to have one of your girls spend a few days with me. A few days, that's right, maybe even a week, depending on how things go along. In my place I suppose or a hotel might be better. I don't really mind. Definitely in Dublin though. Mmmm, what do you have? Well I don't want to be racist but I think white might be the best thing. Tall too, but not too tall. Hair colour doesn't matter really. Well yes, she does sound lovely. How much then does it all cost? I'm not just looking for someone to talk to – I want a . . . well a bit more than that, if you know what I mean.'

Alex listened to the woman twitter on about her clean agency and girls offering to escort gentlemen to dinner parties and all that old flannel for a minute. Then she mentioned the key point – if the gentleman and young lady were attracted then the agency wasn't a party to it and it was up to the young lady to discuss any further dates with the gentleman. All very well, all very cloak and dagger, but Alex thought he needed to know the rate. After all this girl might want hundreds. Not that he couldn't afford it, he was dying after all so what did money matter. But then he thought that he wasn't dying. It's not like this would be the end of everything and he didn't need to care. The mortgage wouldn't disappear into a bucket with his balls. He laughed and the lady reacted.

'Oh, sorry, no, I'm not laughing at you. Not at all. Tell you what, why don't we arrange for tonight and then I can talk to the young lady . . . Tara, OK, Tara . . . about anything else. Is that OK? How much then if she just comes round and we, let's say, eat a pizza together?'

Quick mental arithmetic – one hundred euros an hour meant she'd hit him for maybe twelve hundred to stay the night, thousands for the week. It'd be cheaper to have her drop round for an hour whenever he felt the urge. Still, he might as well go for a couple of hours.

'I'll see her at eight.'

Showered, spruced up, nervous, not in the slightest bit horny, Alex sat on the edge of his seat and listened for the sound of a taxi pulling up. His balls ached though the doctor had promised he wouldn't feel any pain. He longed to take his pants off and sit there in his underwear with his legs splayed out but he could hardly answer the door to a high-class whore in his boxers. What would she think? Three minutes past eight now, she was late and the clock was ticking. He'd spent a time considering his outfit, dismissed the option of a smoking jacket à la Hugh Hefner, decided a suit and tie was a mite over the top, so settled on a nice shirt and pair of trousers. He could have been on his way to a race meeting or a regatta. In an envelope in the drawer there was eight hundred in cash just in case things went very well. In the fridge a bottle of white wine. On the worktop a bottle of red. Beside the bed a pack of twenty-four condoms, though he didn't think he'll get through them all this night. He'd had a moment of deepest regret when he realised that he might never shop for condoms again.

Two hours later he was in bed with Tara and four hundred euros poorer. They'd only done it once – it had taken him an hour of polite and awkward chitchat and a bottle and a half of wine to get to this point. Well what do you talk to a prostitute about, even a reasonably attractive one like Tara. Not that she was exactly beautiful, a bit scrawny for his liking, and being Latvian her English wasn't quite up to scratch. Still she'd slipped off her clothes eventually without too much persuasion and had been helpful enough when he struggled initially. Now they were lying there and hadn't spoken for several minutes. He looked at her profile on the pillow beside him. Her very small breasts weren't really to his taste and her face was far less pretty from this angle. On the other hand by his reckoning they'd just started the third hour, counting from when she'd actually shown up rather than when she said she'd be there, so he might as well get his money's worth. He leaned up on one elbow and said to her suavely, 'Once more, my dear, and then I'll call you a taxi. This time you might do the work.' He lay back down and gestured for her to climb on top. It was better this way. At least there was something done for his money. He'd discovered that with prostitutes there was little point in working. Just get it over and send her home. This second time he even gestured to her to apply and later remove the condom. Tough man indeed. To his list of lovers he added Tara, Latvian acne survivor and only the third of his now seven lovers to have gone on top. It was approaching midnight, with six days to go.

On day two he had a crisis of confidence and failed both to phone the doctor and to find another lover. He'd spent several minutes flirting with one of his colleagues in an honest effort to find out if she was interested in any way in him. She wasn't but Alex was in no mood for rejection. He realised that his only chance with her involved alcohol, however there was no opportunity to get her drunk that day. She said she was off to conduct her adult literacy class at six. Women who teach adult literacy probably don't sleep with their colleagues on a whim. Alex spent all the long day staring at any woman he could see and wondering just why he was in work at all. He thought of a cartoon where a coughing figure phones in sick and when asked if he has a cold replies that he has a headache but doesn't know the sound for a headache. What noise do you make for testicular cancer? Even if you knew it could you reasonably describe it as a reason to stay out of work? After all Alex wasn't required to use his testicles in his job. At five he left abruptly and went home, fully intending to shower and change and try a singles bar. In the event he lost confidence and stayed in watching football in his underwear. He ordered pizza with garlic chips and coke and garlic bread, channel surfed and self-consciously avoided touching his balls until tiredness sent him to bed. The smell of Tara's perfume from the pillow and sheets was enough to awaken the tom in him so he performed a small act of self abuse while he still could. In his fantasy she didn't require a condom.

Day three, a Friday, dawned bright and clear. He contemplated taking the day off but then decided that it might be better to go to work, then to the pub, try to get off with someone there. If it came to it he'd try to get off with everyone there. The day dragged but he flirted with them all, encouraged them to go for a few pints after work, teased the ones who said they couldn't, laughed at the ones who said they'd only go for one, and ended up standing in the crowded and noisy bar with just four colleagues. Just one woman too, and she was hardly quality. Still he wasn't searching for Miss Right, just a shag, so he made all the moves and bought her a substantial amount of alcohol. She responded and he stepped closer. Unfortunately the closer he got the more obvious her facial hair became. On the positive side her generous breasts came more clearly into view despite the rather baggy and high-cut top she wore. Ignoring the looks from his male colleagues he threw himself into wooing her. When it became clear she was chickening out and leaving he took a calculated risk and took her to one side. His explanation of his odd behaviour was heartfelt and heart breaking. She couldn't fail to be upset by his misfortune, and she was. In fact she hugged him and said 'Oh, poor Alex' several times. Unfortunately she wasn't as impressed with his heartfelt request that she help him say goodbye to the little fellows. Her response was something like 'So you think that you can use me to make yourself feel better – is that all I am to you, an orifice you can use while you still can? Have you ever had a conversation with me before, have you ever considered asking me out? No, not even to lunch.' Alex was abashed and frankly disappointed. Women had no concept of what sex meant to a man. If the situation was reversed, he said with the help of alcohol and wounded masculinity, he'd not hesitate to help her out. She stomped off with a condescending shake of her hairy head and Alex returned to face the embarrassment of being seen to try and fail by his fellow hunters.

Saturday morning and Alex had a truly dreadful hangover. The night had ended in a lap dancing club where he'd managed to sport an erection but no satisfaction. His crude hint to one of the dancers had been met with a cold stare and the threat of bouncer and kicking, so he'd sloped off home. The one girl he met along the way was throwing up into the basement entrance of an apartment block and, while he'd momentarily considered taking advantage, he was put off by the smell. Now with three days gone, twenty-two condoms left and just one sexual experience, he castigated himself for his timidity. Never mind that she'd been bursting out of leather trousers so tight they couldn't stretch any further, or that they had been forced off her ass so far that her yellowing thong was visible, or that she'd been saying 'oh fuck I'm dying' repeatedly, or that she would probably have given him a slipped disc when carrying her along the road – there had been a half chance and he'd wimped out.

Time for a return to the certain. The city listings magazine was still in the car and it had ads for at least a dozen massage places. Thai massage had to mean a hand job at the very least, maybe a blow job, maybe even the full works. Thai Palace sounded as if it might actually be a pleasant place too. 'Self-Contained Booths, each beautifully appointed and offering complete privacy.' That would do nicely. Of course there's a big gap between the blurb and the product as Alex realised when looking around his self-contained booth of MDF and shower curtain. The bed provided was more or less a massage bed. It didn't have a hole in the front for his face but it did have a towel across it and could probably be considered clean if it wasn't for a couple of splits in the leather-like cover where yellow foam peeped through. The table seemed very robust. There were four very strong legs with cross braces that looked to have been added later. He was followed into the booth by a slim diminutive Asian lady who motioned to him to remove his shirt and lie on the bed. She dealt very smoothly with him, giving some massage to his shoulders and his back, stroking his arms, squeezing his neck. Five minutes passed and while the sensation was pleasant he wasn't particularly aroused. She told him to roll over and suggested he take off his pants. She seemed a touch disappointed to see no apparent excitement when he did so. His boxers were quite clearly without bulge so she began working his thighs. Alex couldn't imagine anything less sexy – he didn't know if there would be more and didn't know if he should ask. She motioned him to roll over again, this time when she kneaded the backs of his legs she also kneaded his buttocks through his boxers. With a low noise of inquiry she hooked her fingers into the waist band of the boxers and slipped them off him. His attempt to make it easier by folding his legs just made it more awkward and she tugged them over his feet with aggression. He was reminded of an old story where the masseuse seeing the customer's erection asks if he'd like a wank. He answers that he would and she leaves the room for several minutes. On her return enquires if he's finished. Fortunately there seemed to be less confusion in this establishment.

'Like this?' Mai Lee asked as her hand passed between his legs and stroked his scrotum. Her name was probably not Mai Lee but he preferred not to have to add A.N.Other to his list. He was still lying on his face so he nodded. It was true – he did like it. She rolled him onto his back again and smiled as she saw the result. 'You want the full?' she asked, and he nodded. For the next several minutes she used her hands with some expertise to bring him to climax, cleverly catching his ejaculation in a towel and wiping him clean. To Alex the moment was one of pleasure followed by acute buyer's remorse. Was this really what he was reduced to?

'Now how about something else,' he asked her. 'Something more.'

She looked at him with a withering stare as she dropped the towel on a small pile in the corner. There was no confusion this time, the 'Personal Attention by

Expert Staff' had come to an end.

So Alex had increased his count to eight while failing miserably to change his performance with the ladies. This shouldn't be so important but he didn't need to be reminded of his inability to pull women. Women after all are not that hard to get. They have sex, get drunk, throw themselves into inappropriate relationships, offer oral sex in bushes, flash their tits on the street, lose their virginity at ridiculously early ages, kiss other women, wear make-up and skimpy clothing. In short they are available and any man who fails to get one on a regular basis is a fool. Or so Alex was told by a particularly odious and successful lothario once. The arsehole had been right or at least partly right. However what he had failed to point out was that the sort of women who fitted this description were interested in men who showed no nerves on meeting them and revealed no sign of weakness in wooing them. This could never be Alex's way. Still he had little choice; it was Saturday, castration day minus four, and his moment to excel himself had arrived. Alex went to McGowans.

There's no need to waste time describing the place, you've all been there once in your life. Nurses and students, personal assistants and primary school teachers are its life blood. From eight o'clock the hen nights and mixed-generation birthday parties settle in with platters of food. After midnight the waitresses show up. Alex strolled in around ten and toured the room. He needed a start, a lead in, Dutch courage, luck, and for once in his life he actually had some. A girl tapped him on the shoulder and said hello. She recognised him from the local shop, she lived not far away. She even bought his story about the friend who hadn't shown up and better still, she invited him to join her group of four women. He was in, not exactly heaven but still. Of the ladies – it was a birthday celebration for his neighbour who introduced herself as Claire – one was married, one engaged and two single. Nurses all. Nurses! Alex sensed the good fortune and splashed the cash. With the booze came conversation and jokes. He even danced to a fast song, then managed to persuade Claire to the floor for a slow one. If only she was drunk, he thought, and if only I could remember her name. Still at some stage tonight we're going to be walking home together. There could be coffee, a nightcap, a meeting of eyes. She didn't seem to be meeting his eye on the dance floor and she had her arms about his waist rather than his neck, but there was a chance. He wanted very much to pin a number eight on her – nine he corrected himself on remembering Mai Lee.

An hour later he was enjoying a nightcap in her kitchen. Never mind how, just take it that he had basically invited himself in and wouldn't take no for an answer. Fortunately the others had called Claire by name when leaving the club, but she was drinking water. Helped avoid a hangover in the morning, she explained. Especially as she had to work the next day, later that day in fact. It was getting pretty late now and she needed to get some rest. Alex read the signal and wondered what might have happened if he'd made more of an effort with the other single one. Typical of him to choose the wrong one in a fifty-fifty call. There was no time for a brush-off. He had no more Saturday nights. He could not end his sexual conquests with whores and hand-jobbers. Another day of humiliation in a cubicle would not repair the damage done by this stupid woman's ignorance or frigidity. At some point in the few days remaining he deserved to be celebrated for what he was and Claire was in the unhappy position of being the only available concelebrant. For Alex there was a smudged justification to his next actions, for Claire there was only the crushing disappointment of her very worst fears coming true. It was so unlikely, so tabloid, so scare-at-election-time. Every man is a potential rapist and every woman unsafe even in her own home. Except Alex was not a rapist. He lacked the vital ingredients to press home his physical advantage. He was not strong or masterful. He did not believe that he was in control and so he needed to face her away from him and merely tug at her clothing. Incapable of forcing her to act he was reduced to fumbling. He lifted her skirt but could not remove her underwear. He pushed at her blouse and partly opened her bra but couldn't reveal her breasts. He did not know how to proceed and yet he was still driven to complete the act. He undid his own pants but struggled to hold her and free himself. He had no erection.

Claire was too frightened to fight him and too scared to realise the nonsense of his assault. There is no doubt that she was assaulted and her clothes were disturbed. She was groped roughly and extensively. She was traumatised and trivialised. She was deprived of her liberty and her autonomy for several minutes. She was touched on her back and her thigh by a flaccid penis. She was treated as nothing in her own home by a man who deserved no sympathy and had no excuse. She was coerced into becoming number nine. She was not raped, though she could be forgiven for considering that she had been.

Alex sat up in frustration and released her. For some odd reason he thought she might understand that he was simply being passionate with her. Rationalising, he managed to add up his actions and ignore the force he had used to hold her. As she ran from the room and up the stairs he reflected on what had been a disappointing sexual experience. He invented a memory of her encouraging him, he could almost recall her little movements. When she didn't return after five minutes he decided that it wasn't worth any more of his time. If truth be told he really wasn't all that attracted to her in any case, she was a bit on the porky side and her face was a touch agricultural. He called up the stairs to her, said that he'd better go and sorry if he'd been a little over eager. He said he was sure they'd meet again in the street or in the shop and he'd see her then.

As he lay in bed he ran through the count. Audrey, Elaine, Susannah, Aine, Catherine, Maria, Tara, Mai Lee, Claire. A pity number nine was nothing more than a disappointing fumble but it was entirely of her own making. Alex had been willing but she'd been a failure. Nine women bedded, he thought that three more would do it. Any three would do now he'd proven he could pull, even three more Mai Lees if time was against him. The fantastical idea that he had just attacked a woman was so firmly suppressed that he forgot about his cancer and felt wonderfully liberated. By the time he turned off the light number nine had taken on a dreamy quality; she was the good night that had gotten away all because she had lacked the experience or the drive or the special something needed to keep him interested. Claire was inexperienced in love, Alex the willing teacher. She had blown her only chance with him. The irony warmed him and he slept.

No Can Do
Caroline Lynch

I can't
keep this up, this long
steep life, this long
deep fall back down.

I can't
sleep in my bed –
sheep under my pillow,
heaps of yellow wool.

I can't
creep away, or
leap from me, stuck in
seep and suck.

I can't
reap the unsown
neap the gone tide
weep every sorrow out.

I can't.

February First
Caroline Lynch

Was the morning of my wedding and she woke me
by standing over me in the dark – just a rim of light
around her edges like she was dawn, and because
her face was dark, a dark moon, round, and darker
than the room I could not see how she was inclined
behind the veil of her dark phase. Her bare feet
peeled from the floor, she went to the kitchen, moving
between worktops like they were altars and she
a carrier of vessels. I lay in the last bed I would ever
have to myself – not even that could turn me back
into the blankets. She was outside throwing ashes
up into the wind and soft lips of porridge were popping in the pot when I came down to eat, while she
flung washed sheets over shrubs – their roundnesses
like breasts blooming in the garden. Her eyes were
blue among green shoots, arms wide in the whip-crack
spreading of the sheets, when wrinkled and damp
a new season fell out. She picked it up, unrolled it like
a pair of stockings waiting to be filled by thigh. My
trousseau sighed, her mouth lost its needle and pinch
and she smiled.

Castle
Caroline Lynch

It was her father's house and her shelter
from the Atlantic and the Atlantic weather,
but through the wall's thin slits, spears
of sensation, glimpses of light appeared.
Like all those other ladies, she fell in love

and her father did not approve.

It is hard to murder someone in the dark.
The weapon in the hand must hit the mark
and trust the victim's head is in the place
it should be – on the pillow, with his face
turned aside, relaxed, asleep. But instead

the lover slept the wrong way round in bed.

When the axe came down he lost his legs
and it was not a clean death, but a begging
for life and screaming, then the horrible
lurching of blankets through the room, until
they smothered him and flung him in the moat,

followed by his legs, still in their boots.

A banquet then, when the downcast daughter
thinking herself abandoned, married a suitor
whose conscience was pricked by shinbones,
the dark conspiracy wafting round her home,
each man's advancement bettering the good,

until in they came and there they stood;

his boots, loose flapping tongues of pain
blood soaked and caked, arteries and veins
bedded in chopped calves, whose flesh
against the leather made a bloated press.
But then, from all this horror and decay

the ghost formed itself most beautifully

as the most beloved one. Shining, shimmering
looking at her while raising its hand, pointing
to her father, to her husband, to the servants,
condemning them all as knowers of secrets
they all had made, that none of them told

and she wept in the web of her household.

And then she was gone – rising from the story
like it was a feast gone cold, to quietly
climb the stairs twisting up into her silence.
The door closing is the sound of whiteness.
Like all those other ladies she drops

from the page. And words stop.

A View of the Grand Canal
Jack Murray

Eddie was tired of living in a dingy rented apartment that smelled of turnips and boiled bacon. He wanted to buy a house near the city centre, but not just any house; it had to be a house with a view of the Grand Canal.

Despite its stagnant, still waters and rusting shopping trolleys, he loved the Grand Canal more than anything else in Dublin. He could see beyond the floating flagons and crisp packets. Where others saw pollution, Eddie saw the endeavour and vision of the men who dug the eighty-mile channel with their bare hands. He loved how straight and uniform it was. To him the canal was like an anti-river; no big bends, no raging current, and no swallow holes; just a perfectly engineered piece of geography, a runway for the graceful flight of swans.

Before he moved to Dublin to go to college he was indifferent to what the city represented. To him it was a lonely, hard place where country folk had to assimilate to survive, but not him – he was a midlands-man. He liked hurling and his dinner in the middle of the day, and going home at the weekends to his Mammy with a gear bag full of dirty washing. Offaly was the centre of his universe, not Dublin.

But as the years in Dublin passed his happiness with urban life grew steadily, while his strong magnetic link to home began to fade. There wasn't any one event you could track it to, but a whole myriad of life choices that meant he would forever love city life, and remain content to remember home with a warm glow of fondness. He loved the cinema, cycling in the Dublin Mountains, nights at the Abbey, sushi on a Thursday night, and in that wonderfully Dublin-centric way he had so long despised, he loved living so close to where the action was.

But the Grand Canal remained his spiritual link to home. He was a weak swimmer, what you'd call a doggy paddler, but he often imagined jumping in and swimming all the way home to Tullamore. He had a dream that one day he would buy a canoe and paddle the whole way home.

Often on Saturdays he would pick up his niece in Phibsborough and get the number 16 bus to Portobello Lock, so he could walk by the canal and Lucy could feed the ducks. Even though he made this same trip dozens of times, each visit was as big a thrill for him as it was for four-year-old Lucy.

One day every summer from dawn until dusk a parade of flag-waving barges descended on Dublin from the midlands. Eddie would get first mass, buy the Sunday papers and hop on the bus with a deckchair under one arm and a picnic bag in the other ready for a day of passing fancy.

On his paltry wages as a trainee accountant his desire for a house with a canal view amounted to little more than a pipe dream. And aside from his very real financial limitations, Eddie faced an even larger problem that he knew would prove more difficult to overcome: his girlfriend, Nora.

While Eddie grew up skimming stones on the Grand Canal in the middle of Tullamore, Nora was riding ponies on her father's dairy farm in the village of Ballinagar half way between Tullamore and Daingean.

Nora hated Dublin as much as Eddie loved it and she resented having to live there to earn a living. She particularly hated their life in the dreary flatlands that hugged the North Circular Road, Mountjoy Jail and the Mater Hospital, where she worked as a nurse. She was a home bird and was at her happiest boarding the train for the midlands on a Friday evening.

She wanted to get out of Dublin and buy a house somewhere in the countryside where she could go for long walks and ride her horse whenever she wanted. Once she got past the M50, heading west towards home, she felt free. In short she longed for a rural idyll, while Eddie wanted an urban space.

They began their search for a home, both silently fully aware that their respective positions were light years apart. In the interests of progress they papered over the fault line cracks by deluding themselves that a utopian place would present itself with all the urban attraction of Dublin and the peace and tranquillity of a country village.

One day when Nora was unable to swap her shift in the hospital she asked Eddie to view the show house in a new development on the edge of Leixlip. To her it was a bustling town closer to home and they could change jobs after the move so they wouldn't have to commute. Nurses were in high demand and she was sure Eddie could get a job with an accountancy practice or in a company nearby.

Eddie dutifully noted the name and address of the housing development – Hill Crest Lawns – and set out on the journey. On his way he stopped in Lucan, parked the car and abandoned the search for a life of suburban bliss in exchange for a walk along the canal footpath to Hazelhatch, intoxicated on the fresh air and the houseboats along the way. When he got back that evening he told Nora the houses were great, but were all sold by the time he arrived. She questioned him forensically but he managed to hold the line.

One Saturday afternoon, some months and many house viewings later, they both went to view a very attractive artisan cottage in Portobello. Eddie thought it was so good that he wanted to move in that very day. He could see the canal from the bedroom window. If you had a good shot you'd be able to feed the ducks by hurling bread from the front door. It was perfect. They would be in the heart of the city, a walking distance from every amenity you could ever want, yet she wasn't happy. It was even close to Locks Restaurant and Eddie dreamed of lazy Sunday afternoons, eating slow lunches and drinking fine wines. But Nora thought it was too small, too expensive and that they should look a bit longer. In the interests of tranquillity he swallowed hard and agreed, but he resented her for it.

Not surprisingly Nora saw the canal-side house from a different perspective. To her it was too small and the thought of living in a shoebox, however central, felt like someone was sitting on her chest preventing her from breathing. The minute she walked through the door she knew she could never live there.

Then there was the day she saw an advert for a new development in Dundalk. In Eddie's mind Dundalk was like Outer Mongolia, in a galaxy a few light years away from Dublin. How could he get out of living in Dundalk? It took a bit of creative thinking, but he found a way. He booked a viewing time that meant they had to leave Dublin during rush hour. Two hours and fifteen minutes later he pulled in at the house in Dundalk safe in the knowledge that Nora would never want to buy it.

Their shadow-box house viewing charade continued for six months until one day Nora came home from work smiling broadly, beaming from ear to ear.

'Eddie, I know how we can be guaranteed to get a reasonably priced house in a great location.'

Eddie knew it sounded too good to be true, and was afraid to ask. 'How's that, Pet, did you see another advert in the paper?' he enquired cautiously.

'No, but there is a new woman working in the hospital, whose father is a builder, and he is working on a scheme of large detached houses. She can get him to put our names down for a house.'

Eddie couldn't hold his wicked curiosity inside any longer. 'So where is this development located?'

'It's on the outskirts of Carlow.'

'Carlow?' he repeated in disbelief, and in the knowledge that the floodgates of six months of deception had just been unleashed.

'Yes, Carlow. Why?' Nora asked with a genuine air of confusion.

'No, there is absolutely no way, I'm not going there.'

'Why not?'

'Carlow, have you ever been to Carlow? I don't want to live in Carlow or Dundalk or Leixlip. I hate those places. I want to live in Dublin by the Grand Canal, not in the middle of nowhere. The person who invented those pebble-dashed houses should be arrested for crimes against good taste. It's no way to live and I won't do it.'

'But it's a nice detached house with five bedrooms and a big garden, and she even knows a local stable where I can keep my horse. We'll be closer to home and we could even change jobs so we don't have to commute.'

'What do you mean nearer home, change jobs? I don't want any of that. I want to live here in Dublin by the Grand Canal.'

'Why didn't you tell me that before and why did you come and see all those houses?'

'Because I lied and because I'm a coward and I just thought we'd be able to work it out some way.'

His words hung in the air and at that moment they both realised their twin-track highway had reached a definite intersection. The conversation didn't end so much as fizzle out. The next morning over breakfast there was no mention of it, and that weekend when Nora said she was going home for a few days Eddie knew not to expect to see her back on Sunday evening, or any time soon.

Within a few months Nora bought a house in Tullamore with her sister and moved back to a nursing job in the general hospital. Eddie continued to follow his dream of a canal-side house in the city centre.

No Rest for the Wicked
Yvonne Garrigan

Frankie Crane was mad. Everybody said so, even Frankie Crane. He said it all the time and to anyone who would listen. He even said it if no one was listening. Well, that's what mad people do, isn't it?

The whole town knew why Frankie Crane was mad. For years he had been telling people how he was robbed. Robbed of his life, robbed of his home. 'She did it! She's the one!' he ranted. 'But she'll pay the price! Oh, yes! 'Cos there's no rest for the wicked!'

The 'she' was his sister Margaret, the robbery he constantly referred to concerned a neat bungalow near the South Beach, where Margaret lived, alone. Frankie was of no fixed abode, although he favoured sleeping in the back of an old schoolbus permanently parked behind the train station and within sight of Margaret's bungalow.

Frankie had been a merchant seaman in a previous existence, Margaret his only surviving relative. Frankie went to sea as soon as he turned sixteen, travelling the world ten times over in the subsequent thirty years. Every month of those thirty years, as soon as Frankie's ship put into port, he would wire the bulk of his wages to his sister. The money fulfilled a dual function, providing an income for Margaret and their ailing mother and a nest egg for his retirement. When Frankie finally returned home he was expecting to live out his days in reasonable comfort in the house he had paid for all these years. Margaret, however, had other ideas.

Frankie, having spent all his adult life aboard ship, was tidy in his own way, but his way wasn't Margaret's way. Now that he had a bit of space to spread out in, spread he did. Margaret seemed to spend her time picking up discarded jackets, jumpers, shoes, betting slips and other bits and bobs that were the flotsam and jetsam in Frankie's wake. He wasn't dirty, in fact quite the contrary, he seemed to spend an inordinate amount of time in the bathroom, to the point where Margaret had taken to washing at the kitchen sink if she was to make it out of the house before lunchtime or to bed before midnight. Margaret became increasingly aggravated by the state of affairs and the state of the house.

A life of catering to the demands of a sick old woman had fostered a bitterness in Margaret to the extent that she hadn't even told Frankie when their mother eventually died some fifteen years previously. The way she looked at it, Frankie had been gadding about all these years without a care in the world while she was shackled to a physically and mentally demanding parent in a dirty little fishing town. She conveniently overlooked the fact that Frankie had bankrolled her existence all their adult lives. A few weeks of Frankie's cavalier attitude to housekeeping, and his fate was sealed. Frankie wasn't the sharpest tool in the box to begin with and had always felt intimidated by his older sister. When she told him to go, he went.

At first he found lodgings in the town, but with no job and therefore no income, it wasn't long before he was back on the streets again. The vicious circle had begun. No job equalled no money to pay rent. He couldn't get a job without a proper place to live, and so on until eventually he ended up in the back of the bus. Yer either on the bus or yer not on the bus, as the old saying goes. Frankie was on the bus alright but it wasn't going anywhere. As his circumstances deteriorated so too did his mental state, or so it seemed.

The sense of shame he felt at finding himself homeless had initially kept him silent regarding his sister's betrayal. As he wandered the town the discomfort and injustice of his rootless existence festered within him until gradually, almost imperceptibly, his inner thoughts became broadcast news. Strangers, upon hearing his diatribe, naturally assumed he was just another crazy hobo. The local townspeople knew differently. Everyone knew who Frankie Crane was. Everyone knew his sister as well, and over time people started asking why Frankie had taken to the streets when he had a perfectly good house to live in. 'Ah sure wasn't he a sailor for years?' the good wives of the town would cluck as he passed them gossiping outside the butcher's. 'He's got the wanderlust.'

Frankie might have been deranged but he wasn't deaf. 'It's her fault!' he'd roar into their shocked faces. 'She robbed me of what's mine; my home, my place to be!' Soon everyone in the town was aware of Frankie's grievance but weren't exactly sure of the details. They heard what Frankie said but didn't really take much notice.

Matters came to a head one Sunday morning after 11 o'clock mass. Frankie had taken up position outside the church, jumping up on the railings every now and then to rant and rave at the holier-than-thous coming out from their devotions. The usual collection of ne'er-do-wells were hanging around the door of the church, smoking and swapping stories of their Saturday night escapades. Jack Mac, who was nursing a king-size hangover, had finally had enough of Frankie's rantings and roared at him to shut up and go home. Frankie stopped in mid-rant. He climbed down from the railings. The corner boys had fallen silent, for a change, some smiling slyly at the prospect of a showdown or a fight or something to break the monotony of living in this god-forsaken kip. 'And just where is that, Jack MacNamara?!' Frankie asked in a low, even voice, pushing his unshaven face to within an inch of Jack's. 'Get out of my face, you lunatic!' Jack tried to straight-arm Frankie out of the way. 'God Almighty, that sister of yours is a saint to put up with the likes of you. The poor woman must be mortified to see how you turned out!'

Frankie stood up very straight. Out of the corner of his eye he could see the people coming out the door of the church. Mass was over and he'd not get another audience like this in a hurry. 'Yes. Turned out. That's the very thing. This is how I have turned out. And do you know why I turned out like this?!' Frankie spoke very slowly and clearly, all trace of the ranting and raving gone as he looked at each face in turn. 'Well, I'll tell all you good people about my good sister and her nice house, that I paid for. I'll tell you why I turned out like this. Because she turned me out. Out on the street like a dog.' He nodded at them individually, until eventually he spotted Margaret at the back of the crowd. 'No, Mags, don't run away,' he called to her, 'come back and tell everybody why you threw me out of my own house. Tell them why there's no room at the inn for your baby brother, after all his years working to keep you in the style you're accustomed to. Go on, Maggie May, tell everybody here why I "turned out" like this!' But Margaret couldn't speak. She couldn't move. She stood on the steps of the church with her mouth open and her face burning with embarrassment. After a short silence people began to drift away until eventually there were only Frankie and Margaret left facing each other at the entrance to the house of God. And then Frankie too turned and left.

Frankie's campaign, as unsubtle as it was, to show Margaret up for her treachery began to pay dividends. Soon she couldn't go to the shops, or to the bingo, or even to mass without people whispering behind her back. Her 'friends' more and more frequently were otherwise engaged when she called, local tradesmen too busy to deliver goods and services. Eventually she was ostracised to such a degree she sold the neat bungalow (at far below the market value) and moved to another part of the country where no one knew her. She lived out the rest of her days in isolation but possessed of a bitter stubbornness which wouldn't permit her to make peace with her brother. She died alone, her passing unmarked by any eulogy or grief.

And Frankie? Well after Margaret had gone his mental health seemed to miraculously improve. The new owner of the house offered to rent it to Frankie for a nominal rent but Frankie politely declined. The good was gone out of it. A social worker who heard of his situation organised a bed for him at the local 'Vinnie's' hostel for as long as he wanted it; an arrangement which suited Frankie down to the ground. Having spent so many years in cramped quarters aboard ship, the small cubicle was like a home from home.

Occasionally, Frankie could be found sitting in the back of the old schoolbus, looking across at the neat bungalow near the South Beach. 'Everybody has to be somewhere. I had nowhere. She robbed me of my home,' he'd say quietly, 'and she paid the price. There's no rest for the wicked, you know.'

A Perfect Kind of Place
Emily Maher

I am sitting at the kitchen table, the solid kitchen table that I grew up at, a cup of tea going cold in my hands. It's one of the cups my parents got as a wedding present. Most of the service is chipped or broken now so they're using it for everyday. I bought them a new set two years ago, but that's only used for special dinner parties and Christmas, along with the Newbridge cutlery and the pure white linen tablecloth and napkins. I try not to think how many more 'special' occasions we'll have before . . . try not to but can't help myself. If you don't think about something, it won't happen. That's what I used to tell myself. Step on a crack . . . don't say it.

My mother has cancer.

Facing me, Mum talks in short bursts of fear-induced insight. I keep staring at the cup but I can't stop thinking about those distant aunts or cousins, the McRedmonds I think their name was, and their terrible end. I found an old photograph of them at home the other day and remembered I hadn't remembered them for too many years. The more that I think about it, the more I realise that things could be a hundred, thousand, million times worse for me, for us. We have a house – four walls to protect us from the rough elements. That's something at least.

I'm not sure that home means the same thing anymore. Homes are places for improving and DIY stores are the new cathedrals. Wooden floors, feature walls and exposed ceiling beams. What's it all for? God, I should know, I've got it all. The pursuit of excess. And nobody has just one home either. Spain, the Algarve, Section-23 apartments in Carlow, summer homes on the Shannon. And the poor unfortunates who have just started out on the property ladder are already planning their assault on the next rung so they can upscale and have an extra bedroom and an ensuite bathroom. Or an attic conversion. The McRedmonds were far from this property-as-porn lifestyle we live now. Life was simple. They raised hens, went to mass. Their home was a constant in their lives.

I walk over to the window. In the garden (the professionally-landscaped, ten-thousand euro garden, with chrome sundial, water feature and perfectly manicured lawn, flanked by miniature shrubs and decorative ferns) two birds are fighting over the last scrap of bread. On the radio, the low mumblings of an afternoon phone-in show interrupt my thoughts. Mum seems to have the radio switched on all the time these days. A woman is complaining about prices in the supermarket. How everything is so expensive these days. I find myself nodding in agreement.

Mum holds her head in her hands and I put a hand on her shoulder. It seems such an inadequate response. She looks so small. But I can't protect her from this. Why her? Why us?

Do children ever stop to think what life will be like when they're older? Beyond vague ideas like the plan they have for a perfect life? Do they ever think about the relentless reality of it all? The grind and pound of everyday. How they'll sometimes want to stay in bed but will have to get up and meet the bank manager just the same. How they won't feel like hanging out the washing but if it's not done it'll be worse tomorrow, so they do it. How they will have silly fights over who left the immersion on and why there's no milk for tea.

Realities like these don't sit well in dreams. So children just leave them out. I certainly did. My dreams were full of vague aspirations about how life would be so wonderful and rose-tinted when I was older. And it was. Rose-tinted. In order to survive the years, the lonely nights, the boring dinner parties, I simply chose to ignore a lot of the true detail of my life. And all to end up here.

Because dreams with reality are just the nightmare of daily life. And we all need dreams, just like we all need fresh air to breathe, so it's easier to keep our dreams separate from our reality. That way, when the nightmare gets too much we can go back to our dreams for a while. I need a few dreams right about now. And so she tells me between cups of tea how she has known for a while about the cancer. Kept it to herself till she was used to the idea. Turned it over in her mind and dissected it and how it made her feel. Thought of all the scenarios and sentiments and sensations. Such a big word for only six letters. Roll the dice . . . it's a six . . . I'm going up this ladder and then the next one. Six was meant to be a good number. Not any more. Six means cancer. And mother. The significance of such random things makes me want to shout. I don't need this numerical coincidence.

*   *   *   *   *

The McRedmond sisters lived in a thatched cottage on a lonely country road. Ginnie and Martha May. I never knew their first names till Mum told me last week as we stood once more together in their homeland. 'Give them their names,' she said, 'the least they deserve is their names.'

We visited them that summer; two weeks trekking through Donegal, Mum revelling in her childhood haunts. I was too young to have kept any real memories of those weeks, but I've fabricated some from old photos and well-told stories. Do you recall . . .? It was 1982.

Isolated. The cottage stood in the middle of a field halfway up a mountain lane. Outside there were trees. Isolated but perfect.

In the corner of the main room there was a wide hearth and a wooden table stood in the centre. And a vast dresser with rows and rows of blue-and-white china stacked neatly on the shelves. An army of plates and cups and a sergeant teapot standing guard. Beautiful china, Mum always said, that dream-like, wistful look in her eyes as if she might float away from me at any moment. She used to get that look a lot when she talked about home and the childhood vignettes she held so precious.

The time she punched June Brady in the face. The thrill of running across the road barefoot on Good Friday. Scallion sandwiches and the Cross and getting water from the well. Twelve-times tables and Mattie Dunne sitting on his hands and his head on the desk. The way they played with matchboxes in school on a Friday afternoon as a treat. Mum and her brothers and sisters – they were rich as kings and queens back then, but did they know it? Does anyone ever know when the best times are?

I thought it was perfect; it's always stuck with me as a perfect kind of place. The McRedmonds' house. Somewhere to go in my mind when the clamouring thoughts get too much and I need a dose of something simple.

Two sisters, long dead, burned in a fire which made dust of the cottage and dust of them too. A terrible accident. Lives wasted and a home erased. And what it must have been like. Were they asleep? Did they know what started the fire? Did they pray or hold each other and cry?

I was so young when it happened and, although there must have been headlines, I never saw them.

'It was in the papers,' Mum confirms with characteristic distance, dragging me back from my thoughts to the present once more.

And down through the years, when they came up in conversation or when the house appeared to me as I sat dreaming of things that would never happen and places I'd someday visit, I never allowed myself to see the inevitable image – the thatch engulfed in hungry flames. It was too real, too big for my naive childish sensibility. I just thought about the darkness and the smell of warm bread that hung about the place and the feeling of love that house had.

And so life goes. Two innocents, dead in their home, their only home. For nothing. Life is cruel and not much else beyond. And we have pitiful little defence against that cruelty.

*   *   *   *   *

We're in the car and I'm driving. Driving Mum home, to her true home. We've come all this way and I keep thinking we'll never find the place. It has probably changed so much since the last time we were here. Retracing and recreating. Retrieving memories we never knew we'd need to help us live. More than twenty years ago. There are probably bungalows or holiday homes on the land, I think to myself.

And as we drive up the road, past the crossroads and the other houses, I can see that there aren't holiday homes or bungalows, just a small house with red cloth curtains in the windows. Geraniums in the garden. And nasturtiums in the hanging basket.

And all of a sudden, I am weeping uncontrollably. Happiness and sadness blended like milk and tea. And I realise that nothing matters, none of the material stuff we value too much. It's all just sandwich filler; it takes the place of real life. And only real life brings happiness.

That day we visited the McRedmonds, an August day so many years ago, it was sweltering hot. I was tired from sitting in the hot, sticky car and I'd had enough new faces. We'd been in Donegal for four days, driving from one house to another, each with its own set of elderly relatives ready to pounce on me and pinch my cheeks.

'She's adorable,' they all said.

But there was something different about the McRedmonds. There was no cheek pinching. They left me alone so I wandered around the big kitchen. It was cool inside and there was clay on the floor. Soft, warm clay. I was in heaven. Even though it was a strange, dark house, I was in heaven. And Mum was there and the house felt safe. I knew nothing could harm me once I could see her and she could see me. Safety.

We've been here for half an hour, standing still. I touch her elbow.

'We should go. It's getting late.'

'Five minutes,' she says and rests her hands on the gate. I'll follow you back.'

Looking at her back from the car, I see the frailty and the ravaged form of her. I see the heaving chest she has developed when she breathes. But I also see that she has come home. And I'm glad we made this journey together. Glad we took the time to retrace the paths of memory. And this time I won't need a photograph to remember.

from time to time have admitted that she watched Lilly's intake of calories with some degree of relief. For Gertrude had been dreading the onset of her daughter's adolescence – a new concept born of the times in which they lived; a temporary concept, the transient creation of television – the Devil's box and righteously banned from Mount Zion households; and, worse still, of 'Pop' – a provocative, gyrating, self-indulgent noise that the organist in Gertrude could never call 'music' – propagated by Elvis Presley and those long-haired Beatle lads.

These boys were demonstrating an unleashing of sexuality – a concept about which Gertrude knew little, except that it was a most unpleasant experience thrust upon God-fearing women such as herself by the occasional appearance of their husbands' baser nature as punishment for leading them astray in The Garden. Gertrude had been raised, as had her mother before her, to believe that there were God-fearing women who the Scriptures said would be saved through childbirth, thus redeeming and dignifying the whole unfortunate process of copulation, and there were the brazen. The brazen would lead God-fearing men into sin with their flaunting. The brazen were to be avoided and condemned. Gertrude had missed the ironic message of the scripture text that hung above the bed in which she and Andrew had spent all of their married life. 'Occupy till I come.'

And so Gertrude watched with a guilty relief as her daughter blossomed into heftiness knowing that the child was physically ill-equipped to be brazen and hoping that the trauma of adolescence might pass their family by. For Lilly there were no conversations about awakening womanhood, no preparation for the onset of menstruation, no mention of the thoughts that would well up unbidden in her mind, disorientating her and leaving her breathless. And certainly no explanation of why, fat and ungainly as she was, she would find somewhere inside herself a developing hunger for the comfort of touch or imagine the brushing of a tentative hand across the blue-black tumbling of her hair.

The MacNeils knew love in the sense that a puppy dog knows love. Their needs for food, for shelter, and for entertainment, such as it was, were met within a family unit for whom such needs were easily quantifiable and more than affordable. Intimacy, however, was beyond them. Somewhere on their long evolution through history the MacNeil tribe had traded certainty of belief and solid conviction for the fragility of being that allows souls to dance naked in each other's warmth. So Lilly did not expect more than she received. She did not unburden herself of either her alienation from the world around her or of her ever-deepening sense of her physical self. Like her mother before her she prepared to cordon off areas of incomprehension both within herself and externally, in the scary place beyond her well-set boundaries. She would become a watcher, protected from participation by her physical dimensions, and she would develop simple needs that could be easily satisfied within the purchasing power of a regular civil service or similar income. Then came the falling, and her world changed for ever.

For many years Lilly could not bring herself to articulate the moment. Could not approach it head on in her conscious living. Only in her subconscious did she relive the falling again and again in images that were never painted in colour. In landscapes that were always wrapped in fog and inky darkness. Alongside monsters who only hinted at presence, but whose absence was more terrifying still.

When awake she was only aware of the pain. Only aware of the fact that there were sounds (like the slamming of a car door) or smells (like the slightly fetid whiff of three-day-worn underpants mingled with male sweat) or words (like don't you dare tell; like our secret; like you made me do it) that could send her into a state of fugue that lasted for days. She could only remember that she had occupied her mind with thoughts of winter; of the feel of snow underfoot; of the crispness in the air and the redness of noses in the chill; of the crackling of a fire; of the sound of laughter around the Christmas table; of the smell of mince pies. She had occupied her mind with safe places, with familiar smells and sounds. She had blocked out as far as she could the intrusion of his smells and his sounds. Even then she knew that her mind must remain her own place. Her secret space. She had occupied. Till he came.

Lilly does not sleep again that night. The dream has unsettled her one more time. She cleans her little flat though it does not need cleaning, makes herself several cups of tea that end up undrunk and cluttering the clean but faded surfaces that define the confines of the world that is secure to her, and pores over old memories, searching every crevice in her soul for something that might offer redemption or escape, but finding only silence.

By three o'clock in the afternoon it is time to prepare for work. She's on an earlier shift now and likes to get started before five. And it's a long bus ride into town, and she needs to protect her stall. She takes care with her clothes. It's harder than it used to be to look presentable and age is beginning to take its toll. The weight that she worked so hard to lose is beginning to creep back on again. She'll have to retire soon, she knows it and the thought brings her some pleasure – she has a little laid by and her needs will be cheap ones. They always have been.

The day of the falling had begun like any ordinary Saturday – homework in the morning, punctuated by a trip to the local bakery to purchase her daily Cream Dan. Lilly loved Cream Dans and often braved the possibility of after-school detention when, driven by the pangs of a deeper hunger than she understood, she would, in her morning break time, sneak out through the wrought iron gates of Greymount Girls' Secondary Modern and hurry as fast as her oversized legs would allow her to Brown's bakery. And there, for just five minutes, she could imagine herself to be satisfied as she sank her teeth into the creamy softness of the Dan, before hurrying back to the most tangible scene of her loneliness. To the fat-girl catcalls that had become the soundtrack to her life.

Lunch came and went and the afternoon passed slowly. She had no friends with whom she could go window shopping, play records or discuss the first fumblings of innocent intimacy that so enthralled the teenage mind, and so her days were longer than they should have been, with each minute a drawn-out monument to a life that never was. To a time that should have been. And anyway, she was not allowed to own records, and there never was any fumbling before the falling, and the mannequins in the pretty window pictures were never shaped in such a way as she.

She was to baby sit that evening. She was often volunteered but rarely consulted, but that was how it was in 1969 and she didn't mind. And in any event it got her out of the house for a while, and she could enjoy what was almost company for a few hours before she sent the twins to bed.

Catherine and Margaret. Twelve years old, not much younger than herself really but inhabitants of another world. They were confident and athletic. Blonde and vivacious. And above all, beautiful. They did not attend Greymount Secondary Modern – having passed their eleven plus examination they were high-flying academics at one of Belfast's top grammar schools. These were children who knew all that had passed Lilly by and who rejoiced in all that living could be and become.

'Can I drive you home, Lilly?'

Jim Brennan was a big man. He had none of the lithe athleticism of his daughters or his wife though apparently he used to play football for Parkend back in his youth. Hardly Arsenal, but he talked as if it was the next best thing. A goalie. That's what he'd told them. He was a goalie. His life, however, had run aground early and he was facing redundancy from the factory. He lacked the skills to be readily redeployed and 1969 was not a bright year for the North so there were no ready-made employment opportunities. Jim had no idea what he would do now and he wore his frustration like a badge. Fifty-one is too young to become useless.

'Here's the money, Lilly. Thanks so much for doing this, Sweetheart. We really appreciate it.'

Elizabeth Brennan. A truly graceful woman. Clearly the mother of her daughters. Articulate and enthusiastic, and a recent addition to the Mount Zion community – though Jim wanted no part of his wife's new-found 'Bible-bashing hobby'. Elizabeth was one of the few adults who had communicated with Lilly and had to some degree understood her alienation, and Lilly had returned her interest with a devotion that went far beyond Elizabeth's expectations. Lilly felt a fierce loyalty to Elizabeth and to her family; Elizabeth had become her idol, her heroine.

'Thanks, Mr Brennan, a lift would be great. And any time you need me, Mrs Brennan, just let me know.'

Four-thirty and she's on the bus. It's been a strange day, but then it always is when she dreams the dream. She feels as if Bryoni has been calling out to her, reminding her of her shame, or filling the space between them with some kind of sacramental connection. She doesn't know what she feels. She just knows that the dream leaves her confused and in pain. Always.

She gets off at the top of Adelaide Street. She remembers years ago when she worked in the more salubrious surroundings of a south Belfast red brick. When she moved in the company of cleaner and more prosperous clients than those who fill her diary now. She smiles as she remembers the Mercedes and the BMW soft tops and the discreetly wrapped presents purchased on the company credit card. But now she's located in Adelaide Street, street of the carparks and the dilapidated, decaying old office blocks that would soon fall foul of the developers' wrecking balls. She manages a weak smile at the pun.

It happened so quickly and after it was over she knew only tears. When it was over Jim Brennan had stolen her youth. Taken her innocence and buried it amongst the carnage of his own lost manhood. In an act of the deepest violation of both her secret and her public self he had used her savagely to assuage his own diminished sense of being. To rediscover the powerful feelings that he assumed were his by right. He had not even kissed her mouth.

He had turned the car into a deserted parking lot at the bottom of Cavehill; had looked at her with an expression she could neither read nor understand as he killed the engine. And then with unseeing eyes, and with an almost robotic determination he had raped her. And even the stars hid themselves behind clouds.

And after it was over he would still be facing redundancy. After it was over he would still be fifty-one. After it was over and she was weeping Jim Brennan would still be trapped in the frustration that had become his times, and carrying his own shame. Though he would never accept any blame, or admit that the crime had taken place. Even as he zipped himself up he was accusing her of leading him astray. Telling her that she had seduced him. Demanding her silence and cementing her sense of shame.

Lilly MacNeil was seventeen when she fell from grace. The year was 1969, the place was Belfast. There was no worse time, no worse place for falling.

There's something familiar now to hold on to. The usual faces appear out of the usual office doors at the end of a corporate day. The usual suits open the usual car doors and drive out of the usual car parks at appropriate times. Lilly knows them all by sight, and one or two to say hello to. It's a small place, Belfast. A village really. And she's had her stall here for a while.

She's never sure of herself on the days after she's had the dream. Unsure how to explain the connections. How to join the dots from there to here with any sense of certainty. Or how to find any sense of logic in what she knows are the random steps of a life that fell from logic a long, long time ago.

The only obvious connection was the child. She always thought of the child as Bryoni, though in truth Lilly had never known her name, and she was unsure of the spelling of the name that she had chosen. But she had to call her daughter something, even if the only time they spoke was in her dreams.

When she had finally summoned up the courage to tell Andrew and Gertrude about the missed periods, about the mornings spent with her head pushed down the lavatory bowl, about the swelling in her body, she had not summoned up courage to tell them the name of the father. In her head she could still hear the words – like don't you dare tell; like our secret; like you made me do it; that told her that the fault was her own. She felt she owed it to Elizabeth Brennan to remain silent. And anyway who would believe that a man like Jim with an attractive wife and all the usual male prejudices would ever have wanted to penetrate such a body as hers?

And of course there was her hero-worship of Elizabeth. Elizabeth who had befriended her. Elizabeth who had become to Lilly the epitome of all her aspirations. How could she ever allow Elizabeth to hear the shame into which she, Lilly, had accompanied her husband Jim. And so Lilly made a solemn vow to herself, that she would never tell.

Then the recriminations began. The how could you? The we just don't know you any more, Lilly. The have you no shame? And of course there was the deepening scar caused by the wedge that the falling had driven between parents and daughter. Between past and future. Between the safety that was home and childhood and the wild threatening landscape that became the place where she lived the rest of her life.

The Mount Zion flock had never experienced the like before, and judgement came easily. Lilly had become one of the brazen and Andrew and Gertrude were forced to choose between community and daughter, between belonging to the crowd and defending the defenceless. Gertrude was never invited to sing her solos during the altar call again, and though in later years she did reclaim her seat at the organ, Andrew was quietly asked to retire from the eldership, and was never reinstated.

Ultimately however the choices that Andrew and Gertrude had to make were internal. Their daughter was refusing to name the father of her child, and deep in their hearts they judged the reason why. Lilly had become one of the brazen and in so becoming had moved beyond their understanding. The only certainty that they possessed in their pain was that they knew the choice that had to be made, and though it cost them dearly they made it. They would house her until the baby arrived, and then . . . well, then Lilly might have to go and start a new life. Perhaps it would be for the best.

When the child was born, after a long, lonely and painful labour in Belfast's Jubilee Maternity Ward, she was whisked away for adoption and Lilly never saw her again. Though within her soul Bryoni always dwarfed the space. For in those months when the baby had lived in Lilly's womb and her tiny feet were kicking, Lilly MacNeil knew the only true companionship of her life. And when she was taken away Lilly lay on her hospital bed and sobbed the sobs of the truly forsaken.

'How much for the full works?'

Long ago they drove Mercedes and BMWs. Then it was Volkswagon Golfs and Fiestas. Now it's a beat-up Transit Van.

He's late fifties, overweight and in need of a wash. He haggles over the price, but she needs the money and concedes quickly. This stall comes at a price that she has to meet or suffer the consequences. And when you're fifty-one yourself and clearly gone to seed you can't demand top dollar.

She knows how pathetic she looks in her blue denim dress open almost to the waist. She knows how obvious she appears. And deep inside she knows it was always that way. Even back when she wore fur round her shoulders and silk stockings on her shapely legs. She knows how transient her slender shape had been. And she knows the price that she paid to achieve that shape.

In the long aftermath of her falling Lilly MacNeil had eventually indeed approximated to beauty as her weight fell away in the months when she lay on a cot in the Purdysburn psychiatric hospital. The pain of her separation from home and family had left her lost and mentally ravaged and one day she had simply given up the fight.

For a while after the birth and immediate loss of Bryoni she had tried to start a new life for herself. A life for which she had had little preparation. On discovering her entitlement to grant aid and a small subsistence allowance she had found lodgings in a student hostel in Belfast's Howard Street, and had tried to pick up the fractured pieces of her education. She made no more friends in the hostel than she had at Greymount Secondary Modern, and loneliness coupled with the total sense of loss that was now dominating her life had led to the inevitable consequences. She had been dreaming the dream every night for several years, and one morning she had just stayed huddled on the end of her bed, rocking and sobbing until the tenant in the next room had called for emergency medical assistance.

When she emerged after fourteen long months in care she had shed weight and gained a new hard shell around her secret soul. Somehow, continuing with her O-level studies at Renshaw's, the crammer in Botanic Avenue, had lost its appeal for Lilly, and so armed with her lack of qualifications and more user-friendly appearance she went to work as an escort. She discovered that Lilly lite was popular enough with the punters, and her self esteem was so damaged that she felt there was nowhere further to fall. In her own mind she had done the right thing at the time by not naming Jim as the father of her child. But her love and hero-worship of Elizabeth had demanded a heavy price and anyway now she knew that no one would believe her if she had tried at a later stage to retell the tale. Maybe no one would have believed her at the time either. Lilly would never know.

And so she worked her way downwards through the layers of the Belfast pay-for-sex industry as age and cynicism gradually took their toll. And if the fact that she had become what people at the time of her falling had assumed that she already was struck her as ironic she had nobody with whom to share the joke.

Price settled he drives the van round the corner towards a distant and empty parking lot. Lilly has been here before this evening. Twice. The scenery won't have changed.

Her thoughts are somewhere else. She is remembering, as she has all day, the kicking of a tiny foot in her womb. The shape of the bulge on her distended stomach skin as Bryoni moved and turned. The feeling of companionship that was hers for so short a time. Her only understanding of love in a life full of pain. She remembers her dream, and once again has to stifle a sob. He doesn't notice the sound.

'This OK for you darlin? You're going to really enjoy what's coming, you know.'

Lilly has heard it all before. Every corny self-aggrandising line. Every guilt-reducing cliché.

She begins to mindlessly undo the few unopened buttons on her blue denim dress. To draw the shutters on her conscious thought. To find the place where she wants to go.

She tries to occupy her mind with thoughts of winter; of the feel of snow underfoot; of the crispness in the air and the redness of noses in the chill; of the crackling of a fire; of the sound of laughter around the Christmas table; of the smell of mince pies. She tries to occupy her mind with safe places, with familiar smells and sounds. So she blocks out as far as she can the intrusion of his smells and his sounds. After all this time she knows that her mind must remain her own place. Her secret space. So she occupies. Till he comes.

Water Memory
Kathleen Murray

A team of psychologists and scientists from the University of Shukrania carried out a complex experiment concerning water and its properties. The experiment required a number of students, in shifts of four hours, to curse at a large jar of water, continuing over two full days. These students were recruited for their capacity to emit a continual effluent of bad language. This cursed water was then used to irrigate a set of seedlings; a comparable set of seedlings received what was referred to as neutral water. The results were, if not remarkable, at least statistically significant. Only forty-eight per cent of those seeds that had been watered with aggressive obscenities sprouted whilst among those seeds that had been watered with neutral water, sixty-three per cent sprouted.

The cursed-water experiment was the most tangible of the water memory experimental suite. A second group of scientists from the natural history ichthyology department had yet to develop a viable methodology for testing their theory about the relationship between colour and water memory. At this stage they were attempting to extract eyes from fish to be transplanted into a human, affording the opportunity to perceive the water through a different lens. They posited that the fish could read water, as certain people read landscape. However as certain people are illiterate when it comes to reading landscape, contours and songlines, it was impossible to determine which fish species would have the requisite levels of literacy. At that very moment, a man wearing goggles containing opossum pipefish eyes was immersed in a tank filled with seawater.

Water sound memory was the theoretical branch with most currency due to the popularity of wave theories in general. Transmitting sounds to jars of amniotic fluid and then recording their reaction to similar and dissimilar noises a day later had as yet yielded no verifiable results. This theory held that amniotic fluid might be the least contaminated in relation to holding a large sound-memory bank. If sea or lake water was holding sound memories how could the scientists even begin to distinguish one millennium from the next; the sound-memory of freezing, of melting, of flowing, of gradual evaporation and all the conversations in between?

It was rumoured that one eminent professor had committed his life's opus – *Male Pregnancy and the Collective Unconscious of the Seahorse Population* – to a glass of water that had stood on his desk for seven years, staking his reputation on the ability of water to remember in the first place, and to be communicable with in the second. His more cynical critics felt that a glass of water was the fitting watery grave for the professor's theories.

These types of experiments were carried out on a continual basis and had as yet no application or impact beyond the confines of the laboratory, the conference, the journal. However, given the success of the first seed experiment, it was decided to obtain water from a holy well to ascertain whether sustained cursing would have a similar impact upon holy water.

After conducting an initial scoping exercise, the scientists fixed their sights on a small but reputable holy well in a seaside town, approximately two hours away. According to local lore this water had properties associated with the healing of sight-related ailments. Apparently a holy woman, in the course of a holy journey, had developed an eye affliction passing through this town. Her eyelashes had fallen off and as a result, the grit and dust were assailing her eyeballs. She had stopped on the outskirts of the town and bathed her eyes in the spring and on awakening the next morning, she could bat with the best of them. She retained this second set of eyelashes until after her death when her eyelashes were removed, this time by human hands, and sold as relics. It was rumoured that a third set had grown back after her death, longer and more lustrous than the previous two but with lethally sharp tips.

To progress their proposal, the research team approached the Springkeeper who referred their request on to the Council for Overseeing Civic Affairs. She had a dual purpose in referring the request on in this manner; firstly it was an orderly town and affairs that pertained in any small way to the collective rather than the individual were to be referred to the Council; secondly, by doing this, she was causing the request to be deferred indefinitely. The scientists approached the Council for Overseeing Civic Affairs for permission to remove a large jar of water from the holy well to the university for experimentation. In doing so they set in motion a process that brought some short-term ill-gotten gains to one person, broke up the engagement of two others, revived a dormant interest in marching bands, had unforeseen side-effects on a number of other characters and ultimately brought prosperity to a coastal town.

To consider the request, the Council for Overseeing Civic Affairs formed a Delegation. The formation and membership of this Delegation was a foregone conclusion. It consisted of a builder who owned a significant amount of land in the district, had built most of the townspeople's homes and the new council meeting hall. The second delegate was a young woman who had been elected onto the council due to the death of her father – a well-respected, sensible local politician. The third delegate was the administrator of the council. Each brought something to the table that was guaranteed to stymie, hold up, prolong and generally impede any issue under consideration. The builder contributed the fruit of his mighty ego and related pomposity and a desire to negatively engage with anything that did not directly contribute to his overflowing coffers; the young woman, attempting to honour the memory of her dearly departed father, had no idea what stance he would have adopted, therefore joined every committee and delegation and equivocated endlessly; the administrator contributed a labyrinthine knowledge of procedures and precedent and an unerring ability to anticipate the multitudinous effects of taking any decision. This triumvirate had formed numerous previous Delegations at home and abroad; *Studying the Impact and Potential of Giant Water Mills on Local Energy Generation; Pyramids – Changing the Face of the Graveyard; The Possibility of Hosting a World Ice-Cream Festival; The Efficiency and Effectiveness of Chinese Fishing Nets in the Harbour.*

Months passed, meetings, recesses, reports, roundtables, presentations.

Eventually with the research grant expiration date looming, the research team were forced to come up with an alternative plan, devastating in its simplicity.

Many years back a cover had been placed on the well and the only key was in the possession of the Springkeeper. Her position was one handed down through generations, carrying with it a certain amount of honour and responsibility. She had four daughters and it was clear that the third daughter had the aptitude and interest to carry on the traditional role. The job required good judgement that was innate but honed in experience.

The head scientist approached the Springkeeper, offering her a bribe. She refused the bribe and believed that was the end of the matter. At this stage the team had spent an amount of time in the town and were familiar, even friendly, with the populace. The second daughter had a fiancé who was feckless and more than willing to accept a bribe. He stole the key, lifted the cover and removed a large container of water from the well. He delivered the contents to the team and pocketed his reward. The next day he took a trip up to a big town and bought a large and expensive watch. When he showed off his new purchase to his future bride, she saw reflected in its ticking hands and shiny surfaces a life ticking away stylishly but without substance, and promptly broke off the engagement with her feckless fiancé.

The jar was placed in a laboratory and subjected to a stream of obscenities, curses and profanities for two days. In another laboratory the scientists were preparing the two trays of seedlings for the next phase of the experiment. As the jar of water had to last for the lifetime of the experiment, only a small quantity from the contaminated holy water was carefully dropped onto the green shoots each morning.

Back in the town, the feckless man, wearing his large, new, shiny watch was confessing his crime to the Springkeeper in a futile effort to regain his first and possibly only love. What a dilemma. If she reported his misdemeanour to the Council for Overseeing Civic Affairs, the feckless fiancé would be severely punished. The Delegation at this point had formed three subgroups to examine all facets of the research proposal and would look unkindly on the theft that undermined their authority and raison d'être. More significantly for the Springkeeper, she believed that water needed to be returned to the well as quickly as possible. The Delegation could hold this process up with their deliberations.

Realising she had little time to waste in her efforts to regain the precious water, she fixed on an initial plan to recover the jar. Under severe duress, the feckless fiancé was dispatched to the University. Lounging around the perimeter wall, he recognised a kindred spirit – a vain security guard who was spending most of his time shirking his duties. He would march in a purposeful manner away from the guards' hut, occupied by his supervisor, until he turned a corner, where he could sit up against a wall staring into the distance, planning extravagant banquets. His ambition to become a master chef was undermined by his desire to wear what he considered superior uniforms. This vanity was the cause of his dismissal from a number of kitchens, turning up for work with his white coat and hat bedecked with medals, ribbons and gold brocade. Using the large shiny watch as a bribe, the feckless fiancé managed to secure the complicity of the guard with little difficulty. Within the hour, the feckless fiancé was heading for home in possession of the water. This episode cemented his philosophical approach to life, that positive outcomes were rarely connected to effort expended, and hardened his feckless attitude. The security guard's fate was also sealed by the transaction, more specifically the acquisition of the watch. His supervisor, already frustrated with his sloth and vanity, became exasperated by the constant fiddling, winding, cleaning and preening of the watch. Suppressing his desire to pinch the watch-wearing arm, he fired the security guard.

If life took a linear path and if there was any justice, the feckless fiancé, for his initial selfish action, would suffer some painful affliction – possibly pertaining to ingrown eyelashes or a straightforward mote in his eye – and would mend his feckless ways. However once his broken heart mended, he began dating the shop-girl who had sold him the watch. She was impressed by his apparent disregard for money and flamboyance. He finished out his days surrounded by children and grandchildren living in comfortable circumstances. It is, of course, entirely possible that when he reached the eternity of paradise, he was seated in the section with restricted viewing.

With the water returned, the Springkeeper kept the jar at the bottom of the wardrobe, beside a hatbox; the hat she had worn on her honeymoon trip with a cerise wool suit and the daintiest cerise shoes.

The Springkeeper had requested a copy of the research proposal still under discussion by the Delegation. Reading through the proposal the true magnitude of the situation revealed itself. The document contended that,

> *The request for the holy water is located in the wider context of the study of water memory, the converse effects of obscenities on men and women and ultimately warfare and language. Foul language contains sacred words. In ancient times men used these words in times of special rituals to call for their virile essence. However they were allowed to use these words only sixteen days a year. So whenever these sacred words are used for no reason in everyday life, this immediately leads to sexual dysfunctions, i.e. impotence. If a woman uses these words in her daily speech, she slowly begins transforming into a man, becoming hairier and more muscular.*

Furthermore, to add to the Springkeeper's misery, the ultimate aim of the experiment was to contribute to the building of new resources for warfare. The chief scientist believed and had scientifically proven that foul language (and therefore the water that remembers it) was very effective in times of war.

Clearly the water from the jar could not be poured back in the well untreated; equally it could not be thrown away. Returned to the well, what impact would it have on future recipients? Would squinting women leave, eyes straightened, stroking their newly acquired smig? Would blind men leave, blinking in the sunlight, whilst their sun had set forever on other horizons? Throwing it away could release powers into the earth that were at this point unknown and consequently unmanageable.

It was her responsibility alone to resolve the conflicting imperatives. She searched her mind for any piece of wisdom or sense she could apply to her predicament; she drew on the deep store of knowledge passed down through her family but could think of no comparable situation.

Many people who visited the well were reverent, even on occasions dropping to their knees and praying. But the Springkeeper was so used to its presence, she was more inclined to converse with the water as if it were a neighbour, as if the holy woman was residing just below the water's surface. Even with the cover closed she would call out any gossip or news of note. From the open kitchen door, the clearing would often fill with the strains of a record; her husband had gathered an extensive collection before he died. She would often sit out in the evening beside the well, on an old armchair pulled from the shed, with the cover of the well open, so the longest fingers of the sun would reach down and colour the surface and sides. Sometimes she would absently draw her hand back and forth across the water as she chatted on. The Springkeeper had been keeping the well abreast of the ongoing water-memory experiment saga, even going so far as to reciting extracts from the research proposal.

On the fourth evening, after the return of the jar, the Springkeeper decided on a course of action. Despite her lifetime proximity and exposure to miraculous goings-ons, she herself had developed no special powers. Her solution was based not on scientific principles or an inspired directive from the holy woman, but in the reality of what was possible. That evening she took the jar from the wardrobe and placed it beside the open well. Twenty-four hours of cursing had to be counteracted and replaced. Like a scientific pioneer, the Springkeeper created a home-made antidote to the cursing effect. She placed the record player as close to the open kitchen door as possible, faced the speaker towards the jar and well. As the needle dropped for the first of many times, a chord sounded. And for hour after hour, one tune flowed after another, deep delta blues, high lonesome tunes, red-hot fiddling and all shades in between. Waves rolled across the short distance from speaker to jar, hopefully absorbed just as the water had absorbed the profanities.

At the end of two days the Springkeeper lifted the jar up and poured its contents back into the well, in the hope that the events of the previous days had negated the events of the previous weeks. What changes had been wrought? None she hoped. But a significant change had occurred to the water in the well. It took some time to emerge but, little by little, it was clear that the well was drawing a different kind of audience. The water now seemed to have powers pertaining to sound as well as sight, specifically to music. This brought a different kind of pilgrim. Musicians and music lovers from all corners of the earth congregated at the well. And to be frank, they were far more generous than the eye-afflicted, spending money in the town's dance hall and bars. Consequently the town developed a reputation for music, dancing, general good times and it prospered.

Although the research team withdrew their proposal, the Delegation continued to meet, switching their focus from the initial proposal to conceptualising and examining the implications and ramifications of the links between sight-related afflictions and regional musical styles in a local context.

The Springkeeper continued with her duties, sweeping the clearing and the path down to the gate, dipping in a little jug and pouring the water over the heads, ears and occasionally eyes of the visitors. She kept a close eye out for any unforeseen consequences but grew confident as the years passed that any changes in virility and masculinity were more to do with new breeds of cows, possibly food flavourings and even fashion. Up until the end of her life she continued in her habit of sharing a few words or a tune with her old friend in the well water. When she died, her third daughter took over as Springkeeper. She had married a sailor, a mandolin player who had travelled to many places, collected many tunes and spent many evenings in the clearing serenading visitors, passers-by and a well.

As the Springkeeper was dying her body refused to release liquid. Her skin was ballooning, as taut as a goatskin drum, yet in her mind she was draining away. Her memories became watery. Substance dissolved away from her thoughts, leaving watermarks of gates and walls, faces and hands, songs, all imperceptibly evaporating, turning into water memories.

With the change in clientele visiting the well, a rumour started that it was not a holy woman who had caused the waters to be blessed in the first instance, but actually a conference of blind harpists. With each telling of this story, additional evidence was proffered; one old man remembered his great grandfather telling him of some type of unusual gathering that had taken place on his land (in the process laying down the groundwork and claim to any future tourist development regarding same); another recalled how there had been a strong tradition of music and in particular of marching bands in the town years earlier and perhaps it warranted reviving (he volunteered as band leader); another produced a painting of a blind harpist that had been hanging in his parlour for years and on closer examination, confirmed the scenery in the background was approximately, no, identical to the hills behind the well. It didn't take long before this was the agreed and accepted provenance of the power of the water. In fact people had difficulty remembering the details of the holy woman; her name, was she blind? Did she drown in the well? Was she in love with one of the harpists? Wasn't she a local maidservant who served a harpist a glass of water and witnessed the first miracle? At the end of the day, only water possessed the memories.

Afterword
Home... Cathy's Story
Deirdre Barry

Don't cry, Cathy told herself, don't cry.

But try as she did to stop them, the tears started to flow. She had been OK until she caught sight of the excited little faces of her two kids – they looked so small standing beside her, beside their new house.

Their new house.

She couldn't believe that just a year ago things were so completely different. Before she knew it she had allowed herself to slip back into the past, back to that first day . . .

Cathy stood at the window of her flat, lost in thought. For as long as she could remember, things had always been the same. Jack had left her so long ago now that if she hadn't had Maria and Connor as proof, she'd wonder if he had ever existed at all – maybe she'd just dreamt him up. Because if there was one thing Cathy was good at, it was dreaming. Dreaming kept her sane. For a moment it brought her out of the reality of the way things really were – a single mom in a miserable one-bedroom flat with two kids, no money and no future. But all Cathy had to do was close her eyes and she was in another world, somewhere exotic – far away from it all.

Dreaming made things almost bearable. Just like now as she looked at a leaflet saying something about people helping families to build their own houses. For free. They were planning a build this year and were looking for families to take part. It didn't make sense to Cathy. Why would anyone want to build a house for free? And the families themselves were also going to be building. It had to be a joke.

Yet before she knew it, Cathy had closed her eyes and she was in her own home, she and the kids had their own bedrooms, and it was warm. The kitchen had a door that led out to a garden. The kids were playing out there now and Cathy could feel herself smiling as she followed them outside.

Then she opened her eyes. As she looked around at the miserable flat she was brought back to reality. Good things happened to other people. Quickly she threw the leaflet in the bin. Cathy was always careful not to let her dreams coincide with reality.

She stared out the window and as she spotted the two little figures playing on the concrete below, she felt tears stinging her eyes. They deserved better than this.

Before she knew it, Cathy was rummaging through the trash for the leaflet.

Maybe just this once . . .

Habitat for Humanity was what it was called.

She met with the organisers and spent a lot of time in interviews and doing paperwork. She hadn't really expected anything to come of it, and had started to wonder if she had drawn all this on herself for nothing, got her hopes up just to be disappointed again.

And then one evening when the kids were in bed and she was alone with her thoughts, she got the phone call. She had been chosen – one of the houses was hers. She couldn't remember anything more of that conversation and she must have sat for at least a half hour afterwards thinking about things before it started to sink in and she just started screaming.

The best memory of all this was telling the kids. It took them a while to understand what was happening. That this would actually be their own home. Not another flat from the government like the ones they had lived in all their lives, as she had and her parents and grandparents before. It had always been like that, never feeling like you were ever really doing anything for yourself, never feeling a sense of achievement for anything. Living your life from handout to handout.

It took them a while to understand that things would be changing, but since then Cathy had noticed a sense of excitement in her children that she hadn't seen before.

Things moved pretty quickly after that and one cold afternoon in mid-March she found herself in the middle of a field staring at a hole in the ground, surrounded by other families, all of whom were being told that within a few months they would be living in houses here, houses which they themselves would build. The thought seemed unbelievable yet there were almost a million houses worldwide that had been built the same way.

In the days, weeks and months that followed, Cathy worked on her home alongside teams from Ireland and around the world. They all worked well together – the lads who came up from Kerry, Stephen and his team from the UK, Mark and Olivia, the lovely couple from Norway, Kelly, Pat and Rachel from the States. Some of them volunteered every year in different places. When they chatted about their experiences they always spoke of how grateful they were to have the opportunity to help out. They didn't see it as charity, just people helping each other out. And for Cathy it made the experience all the more special.

Cathy's favourite memory from the build was sweeping out her house each evening when everyone had gone home for the day. Quiet descended on the street and it was just herself and the other homeowners left. She would sweep out all the dust and cement from the day. Proudly tidying up her house even though she knew that it would get just as dusty the next day.

It didn't matter. The sense of ownership she felt at that time was priceless.

She would look at the other women sweeping out their houses and smile. She knew they felt the same.

They were to be her new neighbours. Their kids would grow up together. People were helping them to build their houses but they themselves were creating a home.

She and these other families were building a community together. Proud, strong men and women getting the chance at last to break free from the cycle of poverty they were born into and which had imprisoned them for so long.

She would stand on the street, her street, on those evenings, and know that she was looking toward a future of possibilities.

*   *   *   *   *

Cathy felt a tug on her sweater. Maria was looking a little concerned, and Cathy realised that she had been dreaming again and that everyone was waiting for her to speak. She laughed as she thanked everyone and accepted the key to her house.

It was surreal. She wasn't sure what lay ahead but for the first time in a long time, Cathy knew it was going to be good.

Notes on the Contributors

Editor

Nuala Ní Dhomhnaill

Nuala is a well-known poet in the Irish language. She has recently published her Selected Essays with New Island press. Her next book, due in 2006, is The 50-minute Mermaid with translations by Paul Muldoon.

Writers

Lisa Allen

Lisa is from Navan, but writes poetry anyway. She studied Philosophy and English at University College, Dublin, and has been living and working in Dublin for several years. Lisa has also dabbled in drama and enjoys music, the visual arts and travel.

Deirdre Barry

Deirdre is from Tralee, Co. Kerry, and is now living in Dublin. She has been working in the film and television industry in the US and Ireland for the past ten years in finance, production and distribution and is currently studying scriptwriting. Deirdre is a Board Director of Habitat for Humanity Ireland.

Yvonne Garrigan

Yvonne is from Wicklow and now lives in Dublin. She has worked as a legal secretary for a number of years and is hoping to get into writing full time. She enjoys reading and cryptic crosswords.

Caroline Lynch

Caroline is from Cork and is living in Dublin. She studied Law at University College, Cork, and Acting at the Gaiety School of Acting. She is training to be a solicitor.

Emily Maher

Emily is from Rathfarnham, Dublin, and currently lives in East Wall, Dublin. She studied English Studies at Trinity College, Dublin, and Public Relations at Dublin Institute of Technology; she currently works in a public relations consultancy. Emily writes fiction and poetry and she was short-listed in the inaugural Woman's Way Short Story competition.

Ian Mitchell

After falling from the sky somewhere over Western Africa in the middle of the last century, Ian spent years in Belfast trying to grow up. He now works and lives in Dublin and aspires to write interesting fiction, whilst waiting to see what happens next in a life full of surprises.

Jack Murray

Jack is from Ballinasloe, Co Galway and lives in Dublin. He studied journalism at the Dublin Institute of Technology and is self employed as a public relations consultant. He'd like to write a novel and to cycle through Africa.

Kathleen Murray

Kathleen is from Carlow and lives in Dublin. She is self-employed as a researcher in the community and voluntary sector.

Iain Wilkinson

Iain grew up in Cork but now lives in Dublin. A graduate of University College, Cork, Iain is IT Manager for a bank in the IFSC.

If you want to find out more about any of the writers, or are interested in reading more of their work, please e-mail the project at *incrediblehides@gmail.com*

Copyright Notices